Pocket Book

Special Edition 2015
75th Anniversary of the Battle of Britain

Author and Publisher
John H Harris

ISBN 978-1-874528-27-2

Contents

Contents

Injury, Injury, Classification, Quaternary or miscellaneous, Blunt, Trauma, Penetrating Trauma, Shock, Burns, Hypothermia, Hyperthermia, Fractures, Seizures, casualty positions.

Care of Maps, Reliability of Maps, Marginal Information, The Grid System, Four and Six Figure References, Setting a Map with Compass, Setting a Map without a Compass by Observation, The light Weight Compass, Angles Between North Points, Magnetic Declination, Grid Convergence, Bearing - Types of Bearings, To Take A Magnetic Bearing, To Take a Grid Bearing, Grid Magnetic Angle, Indentifiying a Feature, Marching on A Bearing, Hills and Valleys, Forwards and Back Bearing, Convex and Concave Slopes, Spot Heights and Trig Points, Contours and the shape of ground, Know Your Contour Pattern, Scales and Measuring Distance, Linear Map Scale, How to Measure distance, Navigating Round Obstacles, Finding True North from the Sun Using a Watch, Night March, Finding True North, Terms used in Map Reading, Global Positioning Systems (GPS).

Introduction, Natural Skills, Individual Skills, Using Common Objects for Appearance Method, Method of Judging Distances, Us a Unit of Measure, Aids to Judging Distance, Appearance Method, Things Seem Closer, Further Away, Bracketing, Halving, Personal Camouflage and Concealment, Lose Your Shape, Skyline, Target Recognition, Move Quietly at All Times, Movement at Night, The Ghost Walk, The Cat Walk, The Kitten Crawl, Night Noises, Moving at Night, Night Vision, Your Eyesight, Bright Lights Ruin Your Night Vision, Duties of A Sentry, Sentries a Night in the Field, Use Your Senses, Choosing A route, Always use a Compass, Pacing, Navigation, Aids to Keeping Direction, Observation, Pyrotechnics, Self Test.

Air Experience Flying, Flight Safety, Equipment, Entering the Air Cirfraft, Your Flight, Tutor T1 Grob 115e, The Parachute, Life Preservers, (or Mae West), Headset and Microphone, Loose Articles, Air Sickness, Action In an Emergency, Opportunity Flights, The Air Cadet Pilot Scheme, The Air Cadet Pilot Navigation Scheme (ACPNS), Civilian Flying Scholarships.

Simple Experiment, Cross-Section of Wing, Center of Pressure, How Lift Varies, Lift and Weight, Thrust and Drag, Lift and Weight in Straight and Level Flight, Stalling, Stalling Speed, Stability and Control, Three Plane Movements, Flaps, Advantages of Flap, Trimming Tabs, Flaps and Slats, Trimming Tabs, High Speed Flight - Speed of Sound, Mach Number, Sound Barrier and The Shock Wave, How Far Will A Glider Glide, lider Launch, Control and Instruments, Soaring, Importance of Thermals.

Aircraft Major Components, 1. Fuselage, 2. Main Plane, 3. Tail Unit, 4. Alighing Gear, Airplain Construction, the Sandwich Method of Construction, The intergral Method of Construction, Aircraft Shape and Materials, Wing Layout, Engine Installations, Under Carriage Designs, Undercarriage, Aircraft Controls, Autopilot, Aircraft Systems, Aircraft Instruments.

Contents

Chapter 1

INTRODUCTION

Although, there is no substitute for good instruction given by an experienced instructor, your Pocket Book is designed for you to be able to refer to it at any time.

Should you find any mistakes, in-correct detail or would like to make some constructive comments on its content, the publishers would be very pleased to hear from you - go to the contact page on our web site, milpkbk.co.uk.

Your time and that of your instructors, when you **are** 'on parade', is very limited for them to teach you a full lesson on a topic.
Technical subjects are impossible to cover in detail, we have attempted to arouse your interest by short explanations, expertly written, by members of the Air Training Corps officers and instrutors.

It will make it easier for both you and your instructors if you use your Pocket Book for the purpose for which it has been produced - to refresh your memory and remind you of important facts.

NCO's will find it an invaluable aid when revising or planning lessons. With its help, you will gain a great deal of knowledge and improve your training and at the same time fulfil the Aims of the Air Training Corps, thus making you a good cadet and a better citizen.

Studying your Air Cadets Pocket Book does not absolve you from attending your Squadron parades, the reward for your OC is to see you regularly (on parade), perhaps better (turned-out), better prepared to play your part in the Squadron and hopefully more knowledgeable.

THE BANNER OF THE AIR TRAINING CORPS

In 1962 the first Banner of the Air Training Corps was presented by (His Royal Highness), The Duke of Edinburgh on the occasion of the 21st Anniversary of the Corps.

A new Banner was again presented by (HRH) The Duke of Edinburgh in 1979, and the old Banner was Laid Up in St Clement Danes Church, Holborn London in 1980.

The Air Cadets Promise

This is to remind you of your own Enrolment Ceremony and your obligations as a cadet.

"I, Full Name do hereby so solemnly promise on my honour to serve my Unit loyally and to be faithful to my obligations as a member of the Air Training Corps. I further promise to be a good citizen and to do my duty to God and the Queen, my Country and my Flag".

Please note - cadets do not have to pledge to God on enrollment, and can substitute the word for their appropriate deities or lack thereof

---

**Your Record of Service Book
(RAF Form 3822)
must be carried by you whenever taking
part in any ATC activities.**

ORGANISATION OF THE AIR TRAINING CORPS

The Air Training Corps is a National voluntary youth organisation aimed at encouraging a practical interest in aviation, adventure and sport. It was established by Royal Warrant on the 5th February 1941.

The age at which the cadet joins as a probationer is Year 8 or 13 and normally they leave at the age of 18. When you reach the age of 18 and if you are successful enough to become a SNCO (i.e. Sgt or above) you may stay in the Cadets until your 20th birthday.

Upon completion of your probationary period you are then enrolled at the minimum age of 13 years and 3 months.

Should you gain promotion and eventually become a Cadet Warrant Officer you may then be selected to remain a member of the ATC until you are twenty years old.

HEADQUARTERS AIR CADETS

The Headquarters of the Air Cadets is the National Headquarters and administrative centre for the Air Cadet Organization in the UK based at Royal Air Force College Cranwell in Lincolnshire.

It is home to both Air Training Corps and the Combined Cadet Forces' RAF Sections as well as the University Air Squadrons, Volunteer Gliding Schools and Air Experience Flights.

The Corps is commanded and controlled by a full - time RAF Air Commodore, with staff of Regular and Reserve officers plus Civilian staff based at Headquarters Air Cadets (HQ AC).

DEPARTMENTS WITHIN HQ AIR CADETS

Administration Dept

Covers the role of personnel, accounts/finance, works services, providing pay and allowances to all adult volunteers as well as dealing with the payment of all bills liable on the ACO public account.

Also included is the responsibility for the Finance and General Purpose Fund, which is a registered Charity.

Staff working with the Reserve Forces & Cadet Associations in the Counties provide maintenance and new work services for the Corps 1000 units.

CORPORATE BUSINESS (CB)

The staff appointed to this branch have a major responsibility to develop the Air Cadet Organization (ACO) Management Plan. Drafting reports, preparing briefs, studies and staffing papers on corporate matters. Developing and carrying forward initiatives concerning planning and future strategies. Organizes meetings of Regional Commandants and the Annual ATC Convention. Provides the ADC to Commandant Air Cadets, is the HQ Security Officer, the HQ Training Liaison Officer and custodian of the Corps Trophies and Corps Banner.

MEDIA COMMUNICATIONS (MC)

This Department led by a MOD Information Officer and their staff have access to RAF Photographers. This team is responsible for producing Publicity Material for the organisation, providing information requested by the media and internal communications.

LOGISTICS

The Department is responsible for many of the support functions required to maintain the activities undertaken by the Air Cadet Organization. These include; Glider Maintenance Policy, Information Technology Support, Equipment Supply and Small Arms Range Inspections.

Support Equipment

There are many vehicles used to support the Glider function. The most complex being the Munster Van fielder Winch, which offers a 6-drum capacity giving high launch rates for conventional Gliders. Support Equipment also deals with; fire fighting trailers, aircraft refuellers, cable retrieve trailers and an assortment of passenger carrying vehicles.

The Supply role is faced with tight budgetary limits and increasingly stringent health and safety controls. They have a constant challenge to ensure Cadets are properly clothed and equipped.

Shooting: Logistics Branch plays its part by ensuring that miniature rifle and air rifle ranges are constructed and maintained to the highest possible standards in order that all aspects of safety are taken into consideration and that Cadets have every opportunity to produce good results.
Shooting is a very popular part of Air Cadet Training and to increase the interest changes are being made to the firing positions for the Cadets to adopt three positions namely the prone, kneeling, and standing positions. It will open up greater challenges and opportunities for competitive shooting events.

The Air Training Corps has always been well represented and has shown a high degree of marksmanship at the Cadet Inter Services Skill at Arms Competition held at Bisley every year.

The CCRS (Council for Cadet Rifle Shooting) promote and supervise major Postal Shooting Competitions for the Cadet Forces and the Combined Cadet Force. These small bore competitions allow shooting to be part of the training syllabus throughout the year.

PHYSICAL EDUCATION (ATC)

The team in this department include the staff based at the three Corps National Adventure Training Centres at Llanbedr in Wales, Windemere in the Lake District and Joint School for Adventurous Training Instructors (JSATI), Llanrwst They arrange courses in outdoor activities to qualify adult staff and SNCO Cadets to national governing body approved standards.

The Department also arrange special Cadet courses for parachuting, hang gliding, offshore sailing, outward bound, Nordic skiing, basic winter training and community sports leaders.

Organising the major Corps sports events, schemes and competitions and advise the six Regional Physical Education Officers.

HEALTH AND SAFETY (H&S)

The every enduring requirements to keep both cadets and adults safety in mind has to be monitored and attention to the requirement expected by ACO this is managed from the HQ AC from within this department.

AIR CADET REGIONS

The UK is divided into six Regions, each Regon is controlled by a Group Captain who is a Retired Officer and is referred to as the Regional Commandant, who is assisted by a Regional Staff Officer (RSO) and civilian Staff

AIR CADET WINGS

Each Region is divided into a number of Wings which cover one or more Counties. Wings are controlled by a Wing Commander based at Wing Headquarters. Staff who are responsible for the many Squadrons and Detached Flights report to the OC of their respective Wing.

The Wing Commander is directly responsible to the Regional Commandant for the command, discipline, training and the efficiency of the units in the Wing. See 'wiring diagram on page 1-7.

WHERE YOU FIT INTO THE ORGANISATION

Wing Staff Officer (WSO) is the direct link between your Squadron and the Wing HQ, apart from their normal 'staff duties they may also carry out specific roles such as Training Officer (Trg Off), Physical Education Officer (PEdO}, Corporate Communications Officer (CCO), or Adventure Training Technical Officer (WATTO)

AIR CADET REGIONS WITH WINGS

Scotland & Northern Ireland - *Wings*; North East Scotland, Highlands, South East Scotland, Northern Ireland

North - *Wings*; Durham & Northumberland, Centreal & East Yorkshire, Cumbria & Lancashire, Greater Manchester

Central & East Region - *Wings*; Bedforshire & Cambridge, Trent, Herforshire & Bucks, Norfolk & Suffolk, South & East Midlands, Warwick & Birmingham.

South West - *Wings*; Bristol & Glucester, Devon & Somerset, Doreset & Wiltshire, Hampshire & IOW, Plymouth & Cornwall, Thames Valley.

London & South East - *Wings*; Kent, London, Middlesex, Surrey, Sussex, Essex.

Wales & West - *Wings*; No 1 Welsh, No2 Welsh, No3 Welsh, West Mercian, Staffordshire, Merseyside.

THE AIR CADET COUNCIL

The Air Cadet Council (ACC) acts as governing body of the ATC, making recommendations to the Air Force Board on general policy and overall running of the Air Training Corps.

All civilian committees, Wing Committees and Regional Councils are represented by the Air Cadet Council.

The Council meets twice a year under the presidency of the Parliamentary Under Secretary of State for Defence for the Armed Services.

AIR CADETS OVERSEAS

The ATC have Squadrons located overseas in Cyprus, Germany, and also in Gibraltar.

Over the years many cadets from the UK have visited ATC Squadrons in these locations and there is no reason why you should not be one of them in the future, provided you are up to the required standard to be selected.

WHO PAYS FOR THE RUNNING OF THE ATC ?

COMMANDANT AIR CADETS

CHIEF OF STAFF AIR CADETS

Wing Cmdr, Sqn Ldr, Fl Lt, Fl Sgt, Sgt, Civilian Admin Staff

CIVILIAN STRUCTURE

| AIR CADET CHAPLAIN COMMITTEE | AIR CADET COUNCIL |

REGIONAL HEADQUARTERS (6)

Group Captain

Sqn Ldr (Regional Admin Officer), Regional Staff Officers, Civilian Admin Staff

CIVILIAN STRUCTURE

| CHAPLAINS COMMITTEE | REGIONAL COUNCIL |

WING HEADQUARTERS (33)

Wing Commander (Wg Cdr)
Sqn Ldr (Wing Admin Offr WExO), Wing Staff Offrs, Civilian Admin Staff.

CIVILIAN STRUCTURE

| WING CIVILIAN COMMITTEE | CHAPLAINS COMMITTEE |

SQUADRONS

| Squadron Leader (Sqn Ldr) | Flight Lieutenant (Fl Lt) |

ATC Positions: Adult Warrant Officer (WO (ATC)), Flight Sergeant (FS(ATC)) Civilian Instructor (CI)
Cadet Positions: Cadet Warrant Officer (CWO), Flight Sergeant (FS), Sergeant (Sgt), Corporal (Cpl), Cadets, Probationers.

CIVILIAN STRUCTURE

| Civilian Committee | Parents & Friends | Sqn Chaplain |

The money to support the ATC comes from three sources:-
        I. Ministry of Defence (Air).
        2. The General Purpose Fund.
        3. Squadron Welfare Fund

MINISTRY OF DEFENCE (AIR)

This is known as Public Money and therefore can only be used for official purposes and is strictly audited every year.

Training, accommodation, and flying are paid for by this money. At squadron level it pays for your uniform, rent of your accommodation, community charge, electricity and repairs. Limits are put on the amount of Electricity your Squadron is allowed to consume, after which the Squadron has to pay, A special grant called the 'Annual Grant' is paid to each squadron depending upon its performance and strength. This grant can only be spent on administration costs and the provision of approved training items.

GENERAL PURPOSE FUND (GP FUND)

As a cadet you will be paying your monthly subscription which is split into several parts as follows:-

I. A contribution to the General Purpose Fund.
2. A levy to the Squadron Welfare Fund.
3. A small levy to both Wing and Regional Welfare Funds.

The General Purpose Fund is controlled by trustees elected by the Air Cadet Council and pays for sports activities at Inter-Wing, Inter- Region and National Corps events.

Grants are also made to replace equipment at the Adventure Training establishments at Windermere in Cumbria and Llanbedr in Wales. The Squadron's Civilian Committee have their portion of the levy and use it within their Squadron for welfare projects.

The Wing spend their levy on the provision of hired sports facilities, sports kit and prizes/medals for contestants.

Region use their portion of the levy for the provision of Adventure Training Equipment.

IMPORTANCE OF YOUR SUBSCRIPTIONS

From the information above you will now see how important it is for every cadet to pay their weekly subs. It might not seem to be very important to you as an individual, but when you multiply it by all the cadets in the Corps it will add up to a useful amount.

AIR CADET SQUADRON

When you join the ATC you will no doubt become a member of a Squadron, this is the most important basic "unit" of the Corps throughout the country, as it is where you - the cadet - is to be found.

It is normally commanded by an officer of the **Royal Air Force Volunteer Reserve (Training Branch) (RAFVR(T))** whose rank is that of a Flight Lieutenant.

If the Squadron has more than 130 cadets the officer commanding would be a Squadron Leader.

Other adult instructors will form the staff of your squadron. Civilian instructors are also appointed to the ATC, they are people who will have a particular skill while serving and instruct cadets in that particular discipline or skill.

SQUADRON CIVILIAN COMMITTEE

Each Squadron has a civilian committee comprising of five members of whom the Chairman, Honorary Secretary and Honorary Treasurer are to be elected officers of the Committee. The Squadron Commander and the Honorary Chaplain will be additional members.

Other members, are people from your community, such as a member from your local Royal Air Force Association Branch Committee, parents of some cadets and representatives from other organisations involved with youth and citizenship training, such as the Education Authority, local Police, Fire Brigade.

Your Squadron programme involving non-service type activities will have been sponsored by your Civilian Committee. No doubt there will be many occasions when you are helping at events planned by them to raise funds for the Squadron.

This committee does a great deal of work on behalf of their cadets.

This does not only apply to raising funds, but in assisting your Squadron Commander to run an efficient squrdron, such as finding extra instructors, getting good publicity, building good relations with the community, helping with welfare problems, finding local projects for the cadets, assisting with the Duke of Edinburgh Award, providing adventure training equipment and many more. They will always rely on your support in their projects.

THE ENROLMENT CEREMONY

The first few weeks you parade at your Squadron you will take part in your Basic Training. Providing you attend regularly, you will be ENROLLED in about six to eight weeks. You are then officially allowed to wear the Cap Badge of the Corps.

The Enrolment Ceremony is personal to the Cadets taking part. Usually not more than two cadets are enrolled at a time. It is not a photo opportunity for the PRO or local press to be involved in a publicity stunt, it is very much a personal matter for all the Cadets. The format of the Enrolment Ceremony varies, but usually your OC will have invited your parents or guardians, and possibly the Padre to help officiate in the ceremony. Normally, each Cadet being enrolled has two friends from the Squadron who are appointed as his/her 'sponsors'. They will help you through this milestone in your Cadet career. The Enrolment Ceremony serves as a reminder to the other Cadets of their commitments to their Squadron and the ATC.

RESPONSIBILITY FOR STANDARDS

Your understanding of personal resonsibility for standards is part of your development as a cadet and as a member of the Corps, you will be expected to maintain constant high standards, if standards should fall then you wll be reminded of your commitment to the unit.

EXPECTATIONS OF YOUR OFFICER COMMANDING

The following notes deal with some of the expectations of your Squadron Commander. You must remember at all times that all adults like you, are volunteers, their hobby, again like yours, is the Air Training Corps.

They can run a good squadron if you all work together as a team, bearing in mind that you and they will also have other interests and commitments to work, school, family etc.

THEY WILL EXPECT YOU TO :-

Attend parades at least twice a week or let your OC know if you are not able to attend.

Be on time - five minutes before parade.

Be smartly turned out both in uniform and in your normal clothes.

Read and comply with notices and orders put up on the notice board.

Obey orders - if they seem to be unfair, obey them and complain afterwards.
Have good manners , behave as would be expected of a cadet.
Treat with respect other peoples property, prevent damage and vandalism.
Have a smart bearing, when in uniform wear it correctly at all times.
Keep yourself fit, play and work hard, take part in organised sports and games.
Clean up behind you, put things away - be tidy, don't rely on others to clear
up for you.
Never be afraid of doing more than you've have been asked to do.
(Try to be a full and active member) of the squadron - whenever events,
parades, weekend exercises are planned or the time of the year gets round to
Annual Camp - remember that a lot of people from your Wing Commander
to your own officers and instructors have put a lot of time into planning
your programme, especially Annual Camp.
It has all been organised for your benefit. This means that if your OC is to
rely upon your support as a member of the squadron, you will be expected to
take an active part in the life of the squadron and make the progress required
of you.
Help others who may be less able than you - especially new recruits. Bring
in new members when the squadron is open to recruit, be sure that you are
credit to the Corps.

ANNUAL CAMP

For many years the Air Training Corps and the Combined Cadet Force have
enjoyed the training camps provided by the Ministry of Defence. Annual
Camp has always been the highlight of the cadet year.
You should always make a special effort to attend. It is a time when all the
training you have received during the year is put into practice, by taking part
in exercises and expeditions. You will be a full time Cadet for the duration of
camp and is an ideal opportunity to make new friends and learn new skills.
Another opportunity Annual Camp offers you is the chance to be in a very
different part of the country, perhaps for the first time in your life. Try and
find out as much as you can, what the area is famous for, what is made there,
local customs and history.
Many wings, depending upon the location of the camp have open days, when
parents and friends visit the camp. The day is often planned as a Sports Day,
with demonstrations and displays, many of which are organised by the Cadets.
Some events are set up to involve visitors to make it an entertaining day.

WHEN AT CAMP DO NOT:-

1. Drop litter anywhere. Leave your dirty plates on the meal table.
2. Ensure you leave toliets and sinks clean for others to use.
3. Behave as you would be expected as a member of the Air Cadet.
4. Hitch-Hiking in uniform is not allowed.
5. Touch or pick up strange objects on a training area, report anything you find out of the normal to your instructors.

EN ROUTE TO CAMP - DO NOT:-

1. Leave litter, sweet wrappings, drink cans, or any other rubbish on coaches or transport, you only have to clean it up later.
2. Disobey instructions or orders given to you by your instructors.
4. Cause problems for any of the staff who are transporting you to your camp.

WHEN AT CAMP DO THE FOLLOWING:-

1. Read all orders daily and comply with them.
2. If the facilities are provided for safe keeping of your cash, you must use it as set out in your camp instructions.
3. Lock you locker with a secure padlock.
4. Ensure you maintain a healthy diet while at camp, this can cause health problems which can spoil your time away..
5. If you are not feeling well see your instructor who will tell you how to get medical help.
6. Ensure you uniform is pressed and clean daily, if washing facilities are available at Camp use them it will save your taking home dirty laundry.
6. Do your fair share of cleaning of your living and sleeping area.
7. When doing duties your been tasked to do, don't whinge and whine as they have to be done.
8. Phone or text home to let your parents/guardian know you ok and enjoying yourself.
9. Help others - especially those who are at Annual Camp for the first time.
10. Be polite to the people you meet, especially the civilian staff and those who help to run the canteens etc.
11. Be security and safety conscious at all times, be alert, report any suspicious activity or event.
12. If you are ever in doubt about anything while at camp always talk to your adult instructors

MEDICAL CERTIFICATE

You will be given a Medical Certificate for your parent/guardian to complete and sign before you go to annual camp. Procedures vary; you may have to hand it back to your Squadron Commander, or hand it to the Adult in charge of your coach. (See page 1-20 for example of a Certificate) The reason for this form being a requirement is that the Ministry of Defence cannot entertain certain risks and these must be eliminated by regulations, for example:

1. Condition - Epilepsy. Not allowed to undertake such activities as Rock Climbing, Swimming, Shooting, Canoeing, Orienteering, and Expeditions in Wild Country etc.
2. Condition - Asthma. Whether or not they are receiving any form of therapy is not allowed to undertake activities involving strenuous activity.
3. Condition - Diabetes. Those dependent on Insulin, treatment may not undertake activities involving irregular meals or long periods of exertion.
4. Condition - Heart problems. These are of such a variable nature that a cadets' medical practitioner must judge them individually.
    Should any doubts exist on a Cadets' ability to undertake all the activities listed below, a doctor should be consulted by the parent or guardian before the certificate is signed.

EXAMPLES OF PHYSICAL & SPORTING ACTIVITIES

Rock Climbing, Canoeing, Hang Gliding, Hill Walking on Expeditions, Life Saving, Parachuting, Para ascending, Sailing, Rafting, Offshore and Windsurfing. Skiing: Cross Country and Downhill, Water Skiing, Caving, Sub-Aqua Diving. Athletics, Boxing, Circuit Training, Cricket, Cross Country Running, Cycling, Mountain Biking, Football, Rugby, Hockey, judo, Orienteering, and Swimming.

THE CADET AND THE COMMUNITY

A part of the Aims of the Air Training Corps reads:
"To foster the spirit of adventure and develop qualities of leadership and good citizenship".
As an individual, a Cadet, you are a citizen. You live in this country, in your own town, city or village. You have family, friends and are part of the community you live in. Every community depends upon people who are prepared to work towards making it a better place to live.

During your training, depending on how your Squadron staff plans it, you should be taking part in various projects and activities in your local community. If you are taking part in the Duke of Edinburgh's Award Scheme, you may chose to undertake community project work as part of your award. Getting involved in the community can often be difficult and demanding, but it can also be great fun and very rewarding.

You may find that you continue working in the community long after you have left the Air Training Corps.

INSURANCE

You will be aware that your parents will have your home, furniture, television, video camera and a whole host of other items insured. If you have a Motor Cycle or a Car it is a legal requirement to have it insured — just incase you have an accident.

Most sports clubs, youth organisations and others all have "insurance cover" for their members, usually while taking part in club activities etc. It is costly to provide insurance cover, but you would be very foolish to belong to an organisation that did not have proper insurance cover for their members. The Air Training Corps has an insurance scheme for their cadets, but read carefully the important notice below.

INSURANCE COVER
THE ATC INSURANCE SCHEME.
ALL CADETS ARE COVERED BY PERSONAL ACCIDENT INSURANCE
"WHILST ENGAGED ON OFFICIAL ATC ACTIVITIES OR WHILST TRAVELLING
TO & FROM SUCH ACTIVITIES".
THIS INSURANCE IS FREE TO ALL CADETS AND PROBATIONERS.
FULL DETAILS OF THE COVER PROVIDED ARE CONTAINED
IN A BOOKLET ENTITLED "AIR TRAINING CORPS
INSURANCE SCHEMES" A COPY OF THIS IS AVAILABLE
FOR YOU TO READ IN YOUR SQUADRON.
MAKE YOURSELF FAMILIAR WITH IT
- IT IS FOR YOUR PERSONAL BENEFIT.

OFFICERS BADGES OF RANK

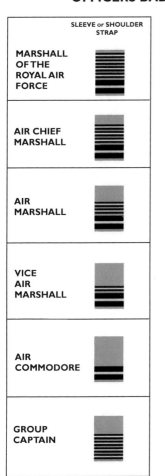

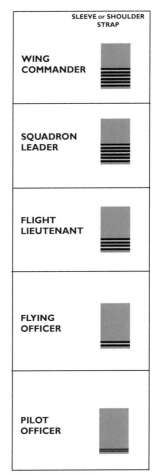

Chapter 2

THE HISTORY OF THE AIR TRAINING CORPS

Like many youth organisations in the UK the early formation of the Air Training Corps was through the efforts of a few dedicated people, who could see the need to give young people the opportunity to experience the thrills of flying.

In late 1918 two men, one an ex Royal Flying Corps Flying Cadet Charlie Longman and the other an ex Air Mechanic Bob Weller both founded the Bournemouth Young Airmen's League. They were fortunate to have support of the then established Air League of the British Empire.

In 1929 it was decided to form a British Young Airmen's League and the aims of this were set out as below:-

"To create a national interest in aviation and to spread the gospel of "Airmindedness" among the younger generation.

The object of each squadron would be to imitate and practice the general routine of a civil aerodrome and the work carried out by squadrons of the Royal Air Force.

The members of each squadron to be classified so as to undertake various duties. By so doing each member would develop a feeling of importance and responsibility, and each squadron would become a useful unit.

Where possible gliding should be included. Members could be granted a distinguishing badge after passing certain "tests"

It was not until 1938 when the threat of an impending war was becoming more of a certainty, that the Air Defence Cadet Corps (ADCC) was formed under the guidance of the Air League of the British Empire.

The first squadron was formed at Leicester in July 1938.

The aim of the training was to "Train youths in all matters connected with aviation" and boys between 14 and 18 were allowed to join.

A squadron consisted of 100 boys, divided into flights of 25 and by the end of that year, only five months after, forty one new squadrons had been formed. During 1939 more than 16,800 boys and 700 officers were members of the ADCC. The General Secretary of the ADCC was Air Commodore Chamier who devised the Motto "**Venture Adventure**" which we still use today.

The obvious advantage of having young men who had received some initial training in "all matters connected with aviation" was welcomed by the Royal Air Force and as a result a close working relationship developed.

Some of the more lucky cadets whose units were close to RAF stations carried out the first glider training.

By 1940 the ADCC was making such a contribution to the recruitment for the RAF that it was decided by the War Cabinet to establish an organisation on the widest basis to provide pre-entry training for candidates for aircrew and technical duties for both the RAF and the Fleet Air Arm.

FORMATION OF THE CORPS

As a result of this, the Air Training Corp was established. In **September 1940** there were 18,489 Cadets in the ADCC.

Throughout the war years the Air Training Corps became one of the most important pre-service training organisations providing the RAF with recruits who were "airminded" when they enlisted.

It was not an easy task for the many volunteer officers and instructors, who were all employed in their various jobs of "war work" during the day or night and then, as they do today, spent their spare time in training their cadets.

The Tiger Moth 7 as illustrated over page was familiar to cadets from the earliest days until replaced by the Chipmunk.

In the post war years there was a need to change the direction of the training and in 1947 by Royal Warrant the aims of the ATC were changed to include training in Citizenship, the promotion of sport and adventure activities.

In the same year exchange visits were started with Canadian cadets. Four lucky cadets accompanied the Royal Tour to South Africa.

1948 a major policy change was made to improve Glider Training by the introduction of the 2 seater Slingsby T21B called the Sedbergh enabling Cadets to receive instruction when flying.

1949 due to the fact that many cadets wanted to fly The Flying Scholarship was introduced taking 250 Cadets a year and training them to the standard of Private Pilot licence.

Throughout the following ten years a great deal of reorganisation of the training and administration took place.

As a result of this it established the future role of the Air Training Corps and many new ATC Wings were formed.

The Territorial Army Volunteer Associations (now named Reserve Forces & Cadet Association) across the country took over the responsibility for the provision and maintenance of those ATC buildings not on RAF stations.

In 1953 His Royal Highness Prince Phillip, the Duke of Edinburgh became the Air Commodore in Chief. During this same year the new Training Syllabus was introduced.

In 1955 it was proposed that control and administration of the ATC would be passed from Home Command to a Commandant directly responsible to the Air Ministry.

TIGER MOTH 7

It was also proposed that there should be a revision of training methods, the issue of battledress for cadets and better facilities for Air Experience Flights.

During **1957** the ATC were the first to have cadets awarded the Duke of Edinburgh Award Gold and Silver Awards. by 1957 in the same year it was decided that the corps would have its own fleet of 50 Chipmunk aircraft, established in 13 Air Experience Flights located at existing University Air SquadronsIn February 1959 the rank of Cadet Warrant Officer was introduced

The year **1958** was of special note as it saw the formation of Air Experience Flights with a fleet of 50 Chipmunk aircraft. At this time there were 27 Gliding Schools and 2 Gliding centres in existence.

In **1959** Flying Training Command took responsibility for the ATC, and in May

1960 the Headquarters Air Cadets was set up at White Waltham as a separate formation for organisation and direction of the ATC.

In the ten years 1951 to 1961 over 58,000 cadet entered the RAF, nearly 33,000 on Regular Engagements.

The new Training Syllabus was introduced in 1961.

In **1962** The ATC celebrated 21 years of "Venture Adventure" Prince Phillip, Duke of Edinburgh presented his Banner to the ATC at a ceremony held in the Royal Air Force Chapel, St Clement Danes Church, Holborn, London.

By **1963** the International air cadet exchange had grown to such an extent that it included the United Kingdom, Canada, Israel, Spain, Portugal, Greece, Turkey, Italy, France, Holland, Belgium, West Germany, Norway, Sweden,

Denmark, Switzerland, Austria and Finland.

During the Easter and Summer Camp periods of 1964, ATC cadets went to RAF Stations in Germany for the first time.

ADVENTURE TRAINING INTRODUCED

1965 Adventure Training was officially recognised in **1965** as part of the training syllabus was carried out at the newly opened ATC Adventure Training Centre at Windermere in the Lake District.

Also in **1965**, ATC cadets took part in the Nijmegen March in Holland.

In **1967** a Review Committee - The Morris Committee - looked at the organisation of the ATC. They made many recommendations; creating ATC Regions to be controlled by Regional Commandants. Wings were redefined to comprise 20 squadrons.

The age of enrolment was lowered to 13 years 9 months.

Additional places were established to enable recruiting of more officers and instructors.

The year **1968** saw the formation of 6 further Regions alongside the existing Scottish Region.

The Headquarters Air Cadets moved from RAF White Waltham to RAF Station Brampton in Lincolnshire.

In April **1969** seven Regional Commanders assumed control and command of their new Regions.

The Air Training Corp's newspaper the Air Cadet News was established as a monthly newspaper.

1970 saw the first Inter Service Cadet Swimming Championship, between the Army Cadet Force, Sea Cadet Corps and the Air Training Corps.

In this year trials were started with the SLG (Self Launching Glider) fitted

Cadet Mk 3 Glider, provide by Stephan Kopelke

with an engine which was switched off on gaining the correct height.

1971 was the 30th birthday of the ATC, and in 1972 Air Navigation was introduced as an 'O' Level subject. The first ATC camps to be held in Malta were in **1973**, they continued until Malta gained its independence and a change in the political climate in 1978.

1975 saw Headquarters Air Cadet on the move again and were established at RAF Station Newton in Nottinghamshire.

1976 Gibraltar was an Annual Camp venue for the first time.

1977 was the Queens Silver Jubilee Review of the Reserve Forces held at RAF Station, Finningley, South Yorkshire. The ATC took part in the Review and also put on a display for the occasion.

The Venture motor glider entered service at selected air cadet volunteer gliding schools.

In **1979** HRH The Duke of Edinburgh presented a new Banner to the ATC. In this year the first ATC camps were held in Cyprus.

Leading Cadet Stitt was the first cadet to fly solo the Slingsby T-53B on 15th August 1968.

POLICY CHANGE - GIRLS JOIN ATC

1980 saw a welcome change in recruiting policy when a scheme was introduced for girls to join the ATC.

The first award of the **Darce Sword** was made to the Best Cadet in the Corps.

Meteorology was introduced as an 'O' level subject.

1981 girl cadets were flying solo in gliders, gaining marksmanship badges and taking an active part in the DofE Award Scheme

1981 4th Feb was the 40th Anniversary of the ATC, HRH The Duke of Edinburgh, Air Commodore in Chief, presented a special award to the Corps to be known as the "Guinea Pig Prize" to be awarded in recognition of an outstanding individual performance.

Girls cadets joined 22 selected squadrons throughout the Corps.

Cadet Fiona BrownNo404 (Brough of Morpeth) Squadron being the first girl Cadet in the Corps to gain a Gold Award.

In **1982** following the success of the initial stages of the trial, the scheme for girls in the ATC was extended to one Squadron in each wing. Proposals are put to the Air Council for the extension of the scheme.

The first woman to command an ATC Squadron No 2500 (St Neots) was Flight Lieutenant Janet Page WRAF(T).

FS James Smith of No 356 (Felixstowe) Squadron was the first recipient of the Kriegie Trophy as the best ATC cadet to attend Frimley Park Leadership Course.

In the same year, The Air Gunners Association presented the Corps with a trophy to be competed for in the pre-Bisley competition shoot.

RAF Station Wethersfield was the first USAF base to host a voluntary gliding school.

Flight Sergeant Simon Burrows of No 127 (Wakefield) Sqn and Cadet Dabiel Norman of No 1013 Sqn (Quantock) Sqn were awarded the Guinea Pig Prize who rescued a friend from the sea.

In 1982 FS Anthony Hambleton, the 1982 Dacre Sword winner was the first Air Cadet to fly in a tornado aircraft of TWCU at RAF Honington.

On 20th September the ASK 21 and ASW 19 Gliders came into service with the Air Cadet Gliding Organisation at ACCGS RAF Syerston.

Ten Vanguards (dual seat) joined the fleet as well as five Valiants (single seat) and two Janus Cs (dual seat). During 1983 Air Cadet gliders took part in the National Championships at Lasham and Husbands Bosworth and at the Inter - Services Championships at Henlow.

1982 approval was given to replace the Sedberghs and Kirby Cadet Gliders and replace them with the ASK 21 Vanguard a tandem 2 seater high performance glider and the ASW 19 (Valiant) a single seater.

In **1984** the first award of the Dacre Brooch is made to a CWO Fiona Brown No 404 (Morpeth) Squadron by Mrs Dacre at a ceremony at Newcastle Airport. The Diamond Brooch is mounted on a blue sash bordered by gold braid. Below the brooch is the Corps motto. "Venture Adventure".

NEW GLIDER FOR ATC

On the 5th October at ACCGS, Lord Trefgarne, Under Secretary of State for the Armed Services, brought the Viking (Grob G103 Twin 11) glider into service.

Viking T Mk 1 The Grob 103 Viking entered service in 1984

They were the first of 100 new dual seat gliders to replace the Slingsby wooden gliders (12B and T31), delivered during 1984/5.

In May **1985** Her Majesty The Queen as Patron, presented the Royal Aero Club Diploma to the ATC. The award was made for:

> *"exceptional service in providing flying and gliding training*
> *and associated aviation skills to cadets 1941 to 1985".*

Two cadets from Cyprus No1 (Akrotiri) Squadron were the first cadets to undertake a glider proficiency course on Venture gliders at ACCGS Syerston.

In **1986** the first Save and Prosper Scholarships were awarded to five cadets. The cadets spent a two weeks course at the RAF Gliding and Soaring Association at RAF Bicester.

The Gill Trophy was presented to No 2390 (Belfast Royal Academy) Squadron by Mrs Irene Gill, widow of the late Honorary Secretary of the Air Gunners Association at the Inter Service Cadet Rifle Meeting at Bisley in 1986 for the best aggregate score.

A new Adventure Training Centre was announced at Llanbedr, near Harlech, North Wales to be opened in the Spring of 1988.

FACTS

From 1983 to 1986 inclusive Air cadets provided some 26% of the annual RAF intake of officers, airmen and apprentices. In 1987, 76% of Direct Entry Pilots joining the Royal Air Force were ex-members of the Air Training Corps or Combined Cadet Force (RAF Sections).

1987 From the 1st January cadets could be enrolled into the Corps at the minimum age of 13 years and 3 months.

The Vigilant Grob G109

1990 On the 1st March The Vigilant Grob B1098 entered service with the Air Cadets, it is a side-by-side 2-seat motor glider, with all round vision both forward and downward views.

1991 Golden Jubilee of the ATC, the 50th Anniversary of the founding of the Air Cadet movement.

Many events were held throughout the United Kingdom.

Chipmunk

1991 A significant landmark in ATC history came in 1991 with the Corps Golden Jubilee. The initial launch of the 50th Anniversary year took place on 31 January 1991 at the Southampton Hall of Aviation when the AOC Air Cadets, Air Commodore Skelley, received the Air League Challenge Cup from Mr Michael Cobham, chairman of the Air League. The cup was awarded to the Corps in recognition of the outstanding contribution made to British aviation over the past 50 years.

On the 3rd Feb, at St Clement Danes Church in the Strand, London, officers and cadets of the London and South East Region took part in the Corps Service of Thanksgiving, held in the presence of His Royal Highness The Duke of Edinburgh KG, KT, OM, GBE, AC, QSO, Air Commodore-in-Chief Air Training Corps.

In March two groups of adults and cadets set out on an Expedition to Nepal, they were from Herts/Bucks, Somerset, Bristol/Gloucester and No 3 Welsh Wing. Anniversary memorabilia was produced, including attractive plates and anniversary mugs.

1992. Initial Glider Training introduced to give young cadets an early chance of actually flying.

1999. A new Aircraft the GROB 115E (Tutor) was introduced for use at University Air Squadrons and Air Experience Flying.

TUTOR
GROB 115E

G-BYUC

SELF TEST QUESTIONS

1. Who and when formed the Bournemouth Young Airmen's League.
2. In 1929 a British Young Airman's League was formed. What were its aims.
3. When was the Air Defence Cadet Corps (ADCC) formed.
4. How many Cadets and officers were members in 1939.
5. Who devised the motto of th ADCC and what was that motto.
6. How many Cadets were there in the ADCC in 1940.
7. In what year was the new Training Syllabus introduced.
8. When did Air Experience Flights start.
9. From 1951 to 1961 how many Air Cadets joined the RAF.
10. When did the ATC first take part in Adventure Training.
11. When did ATC cadets go to RAF Stations in Germany.
12. When was Gibraltar an Annual Camp venue for the first time.
13. When did the Venture motor glider enter service.
14. When were Girls allowed to join the Air Training Corps.
15. Who was the first girl cadet to attain the D of E Gold Award.
16. Name the new Gliders that came into service during 1983.
17. What is the name of two new Glider that came into service in 1984.
18. From the 1st January 1987 what was the minimum age for joining the ATC.

Chapter 3

DISCIPLINE, DRILL AND DRESS

When thinking about this section on Drill, Discipline and Dress it will come to mind that you may have seen Airmen of the Queen's Colour Squadron on television or you may have been lucky enough to have actually seen them `on parade'.

You cannot help being impressed by their smart turnout and the precision of their drill movements. They could not perform to the very high standards required unless they as individuals have strong personal discipline and are dedicated members of their "team".

An important part of your training involves teaching you to be a smartly 'turned out', disciplined and a well organised individual.

Drill is a powerful aid towards teaching you these qualities. In a voluntary youth organisation it would seem to be a difficult task to instill discipline. However, it is not really a problem since, after all, you are a volunteer like everyone else in your squadron, who all rely on a much more important type of discipline - SELF DISCIPLINE.

You will be surprised how you can enjoy taking part in drill, especially if you have a good instructor who can make it interesting.

Once all of you have mastered the movements and are able to move smartly as "one body", then - and only then you will feel a real sense of pride, you will be alert and carry out orders instantly with precision.

As an cadets you would be expected to carry out drills in an aircraft in exactly the same manner. No matter what job you have to do, if you are smart on parade you will develop the right attitudes towards improving your personal standards in all you do.

In the service environment, the immediate reaction to orders given in quick succession - as in drill, will often have to be applied to keep an efficient team together under a strain that would normally break it.

UNIFORM

Another aspect of your personal discipline is your uniform which is your personal responsibility.

The way you take care of it can be seen by your very appearance in it.

Your reputation for 'turnout' with your instructors will depend upon your attention to detail when wearing uniform, listen to their instructions and get it right first time.

You will now appreciate that there is more to drill than you might think, it is a team effort, more precise than the most highly trained Football team. The concentration of individual effort and the self discipline required by you will be hard to find in any other situation.

Once you and the others in your Squadron have become proficient enough at Drill you may appear in public or take part in parades that include marching through your home town often with a band playing you will be able to control the swing of your arms and the roll of your shoulders allowing you to feel the pride in your squadron and yourself - it takes some beating, and what is more you will enjoy every minute of it.

CARE OF CLOTHING

You are fortunate to have your uniform issued to you free of charge. It must be appreciated that this costs a great deal of money to provide all cadets with uniforms and to carry stocks for exchanges. It follows that it must be treated with respect and taken care of.

If you are to be a credit to yourself and the ATC you must keep it clean, pressed and in good repair at all times.

You do need to learn how to correctly use an iron, do not leave it to others to clean and press for you.

This naturally applies just as much to you when in your civilian clothes, your turnout portrays how well you look after yourself and your standard of personal discipline.

All your clothes need hanging up properly on hangers, not thrown over a chair or dumped on the floor.

You will be expected to hand in a clean uniform when it comes to changing it, which can happen several times during your cadet service.

Talk to your officers or instructor to find out the best and accepted method of cleaning it.

It is understood that young people grow quite rapidly at times, your Supplies Officer will have a system for exchanging uniforms. However, uniform supply is limited, therefore it is your responsibility to maintain the highest standards without defacing the uniform with iron marks or alterations.

HINTS FOR PRESSING UNIFORM

Do not let the hot iron come into direct contact with the material..
It makes it shiny or worse still, may burn it. You will then have to pay for a replacement. Use a damp not wet, non-fluffy cloth, (an old tea towel is ideal), place this on your trousers/skirt then place paper over this.

CARE AND CLEANING OF BOOTS AND SHOES

There are different ideas about how clean your boots should be. It is most likely that you will only have one pair of boots and they have to be worn for all your cadet activities. Ideally if you can manage it a pair of boots for Adventure Training and shoes for Squadron activities.

It is very difficult to wear them on an expedition one day and then have them fit for a "drill competition" the next!!

What is important is that both boots and shoes fit you comfortably and are kept in good repair, they are always clean and well polished.

The laces must be straight across the eyelet holes, not crossing over them.

Should you get your boots or shoes wet, do not dry them in front of a fire or over heat.

Leather is a natural material and so must dry naturally. It helps if you stuff newspaper into them to absorb the wet/damp, replacing it after a couple of hours with dry paper.

Always have a spare pair of laces, with you. Only wear thick woolen socks with boots.

Black socks are permitted for males, whilst females should wear Barely Black coloured tights.

Cadets are encouraged to purchase shoes for blue uniform, (No2 Dress/ No2 Dress C and boots are to be worn normally in No.3 Dress uniform or Adventure Training only.

PERSONAL TURNOUT

Males
Face clean and shaved if necessary
Hair not over the collar or ears, sideburns not below bottom of ears

Females
Hair: If your hair is long enough to put up NEATLY, then
do so. Try to keep your hair from 'falling' as it can be a problem on exercise or the ranges.
Do not wear fancy hair slides, bobbles or fancy scrunchies.
Earrings: ONE pair of plain studs.
It is advisable to remove them whilst on exercise, to prevent loss.

NO2 DRESS

NO2 DRESS

NO2 DRESS C

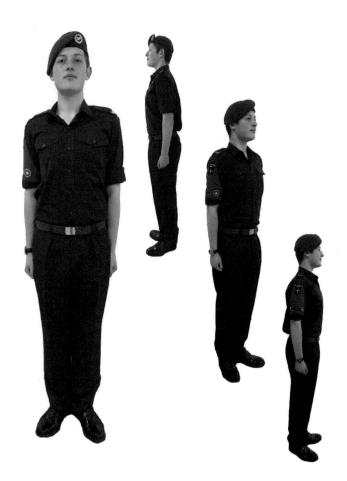

NO3 DRESS

NO3 DRESS

GENERAL ADVICE

Body Piercing

It is your personal choice whether you have body piercing. However, for your safety, these should be either removed whilst in uniform, or covered securely with a sticking plaster.

There is a real danger of these piercings being caught or becoming infected whilst undertaking most cadet activities.

Rings:

One signet ring is acceptable, but 'Rings on every finger' does not look right when in uniform. There is also a possibility they may slip off during an exercise or getting caught when weapon cleaning.

Neck Chains and Bracelets:

Should not be worn when in uniform, unless they are Medic Alert or similar.

When Compliments are paid:

NATIONAL ANTHEM

When on parade, stand to attention, only Officers and Warrant Officers salute, NCOs will if in charge of a party.

When not on parade, but in uniform, all ranks will salute.

When not on parade, and in plain clothes, all ranks will stand to attention. If a hat is worn, it will be removed (Females do not remove hats).

STANDARDS GUIDONS AND COLOURS

As a squad on the march you will give an 'Eyes Left' or 'Right'.

As an individual, you halt; face passing Standards, Guidons or Colours.

PAYING COMPLIMENTS

Visiting Officers will always notice the standard of saluting in your Squadron; it will be their first impression of you and the Squadron. Make sure it is a good impression.

THE UNION FLAG

INTRODUCTION TO DRILL

Throughout history, Drill has been the foundation upon which discipline; teamwork, pride and pageant have all taken equal part.

In the days of the 'Brown Bess' musket, when in battle, the infantry formed a square in their three ranks in order to give effective firepower.

This action was carried out as a drill, taught and practiced on the barrack square. The discipline required to 'hold the line' was the difference between defeat and victory.

Drill parades were hard and rigorous, with harsh violence dished out by the instructors.

Times have changed, all services yet they still rely on drill to build team spirit and to train the individuals mind to respond to orders given in the quickest possible time.

When you are first introduced to Drill Commands, you may find that your reactions are slow and mistakes easily made. Fortunately your initial lessons are all completed at the 'Halt' i.e. stood still. It is difficult enough to stand still, especially when there is a fly walking down your nose - no matter, stand still!

Once you have mastered the initial movements and been taught how to march without your arms moving in the wrong order, you will suddenly find it all comes together, your squad starts to move as a team.

It will probably feel even better when you take part in a Civic or Cadet Sunday Parade. You will be with the rest of your Squadron, smartly turned out and marching behind a band.

It might sound odd to those of you who have not attended such Parades, but it gives you a real 'Buzz' and dare it be said, pride in your Squadron and the Air Training Corps. (Particularly if your family and friends are watching!)

REMEMBER: DO NOT WEAR YOUR UNIFORM
WITHOUT PERMISSION FROM YOUR SQUADRON COMMANDER
UNLESS YOU ARE ON CADET DUTIES

DRILL - INTRODUCTORY WORDS OF COMMAND

USED FOR SQUAD DRILL

Good instructors give *INTRODUCTORY* words of   command giving warning of
what the next word of command is to be.

Many instructors do not do this; the result is the squad turning in different
directions at the same time!

Before moving a squad in any direction, the instructor indicates what
direction they intend to move them by using *INTRODUCTORY* words of
command, before giving the actual command to execute the movement.

TEACHING DRILL

The aims of Drill are:

1. To produce a Cadet who has self respect, is alert and obedient
2. To provide the basis for teamwork

Drill is exacting and strict attention to detail must be observed. You
will need the following qualities to become an excellent Drill Instructor.

1. **PATIENCE.** Never lose your temper.
2. **ENTHUSIASM.** You must fire your squad with a will to achieve.
3. **CONSISTENCY.** Set yourself and the squad a high standard and do not
   deviate from it.
4. **HUMANITY.** Understand the squad's problems; praise
   readily,
5. **PERSONALITY.** As a drill instructor you must impress
   your squad - always have them under control, lead by example:
   1. Always be impeccably turned out.
   2. When drilling a squad, stand to attention, always face them.
   3. When moving, march as you would wish your squad to march - no
      'bimbling.'
   4. When demonstrating, be accurate; never exaggerate a drill movement. If
      the movement is with a rifle use that article and nothing else.
   5. Never use bad language and sarcasm; it is the sign of a poor instructor.
   6. Ensure that your words of command are clear, DO NOT do as some
      drill instructors, create your own 'drill language', it is bad practice.
   7. Do not become over familiar or humiliate individual members of your
      squad.

COMPLIMENTS

Saluting - Origin and Information

The salute with the hand, the present arms to senior offices and the salute with the sword were methods by which the person paying a compliment could show the person to whom the compliment was paid that no offence was meant and they were unarmed.

They were all gestures symbolic of loyalty and trust.

A salute is the normal greeting between comrades in arms. That a salute is properly and smartly given when you meet an officer is a basic matter of discipline.

That the salute is properly and smartly given is a matter of training.

Failure by an officer to return a salute shows a lack of courtesy on their part.

THE QUEEN'S COMMISSION

All compliments derive their origin from the Sovereign, to whom the highest compliment, the Royal Salute, is paid.

PAYING COMPLIMENTS - SALUTING

Saluting to the front - Common Faults

1. The body and head not remaining still and erect.
2. Allowing your right elbow to come forward.
3. Hand not flat and in correct position, finger tips not near to head at eye level.
4. Wrist bent - not in straight line with forearm.
5. Allowing left arm to creep forwards.
6. Left fist not clenched with thumb to front, arm not tight into side.

NOTE As an aid to good saluting, remember your right hand - with the palm of your hand flat, thumb on top, travels the `longest way up and the shortest way down' when you are saluting correctly.

THE QUEENS COMMISSION

All officers in the Air Training Corps are holders of the Queen's Commission, and when compliments are paid by saluting it is in recognition of the Sovereign's Commission held in trust by that officer.

The actual Commission an officer receives is in fact a document on parchment paper signed and sealed by Her Majesty The Queen.

Ask one of your officer to bring theirs along for you to see, it is a very special and interesting document.

DEFINITIONS USED IN DRILL

ALIGNMENT: Any straight line on which a body of cadets is or
are to form.

CLOSE ORDER: Formation of a flight or squad in three ranks (3 ranks)

x x x x x x x x x   **- FRONT RANK**
x x x x x x x x x   **- CENTRE RANK**
x x x x x x x x   **- REAR RANK**

Each cadet in the centre and rear ranks covering the corresponding cadet in
the front rank. Distance of 75cm (30 inches)

COLUMN OF THREES   x   x   x
    x   x   x
    x   x   x
    x   x   x
    x   x   x

A succession of cadets standing side by side in threes, covering the front files
as in diagram above. Normal formation for marching on a road.

COVERING:	As in both of the illustration above, one behind the other covering off the front files.
DIRECTING FLANK:	Flank by which units march and dress, "By the Left/Right".
FILE:	Any cadet in the front rank together with the cadet(s) immediately behind them.
FLIGHT:	A sub-unit, two or more of which comprise a squadron. (approximately size of Army or Navy platoon)
FORMATION:	A number of units grouped together under one commander.
FRONT:	The direction in which units are facing or moving at any given time.
FRONTAGE:	The extent of ground covered laterally by a body or bodies of cadets.
GUARD OF HONOR:	A parade not exceeding 100 cadets formed to present formal ceremonial compliments to royal or residential persons.
'HALF GUARD':	A parade not exceeding 50 cadets formed to present ceremonial compliments to other particular distinguished persons.

INCLINE: Half a turn, you move through 45°

FILE x x   **SINGLE FILE** x

       x x   x

       x x   x

Cadet formed up in pairs,   Single cadets formed up
covering off the front file.   Covering off the front
cadet.

MARKER:	An NCO or cadet positioned to mark a point where the flank of a squad or unit is to rest/dress.
OPEN ORDER:	Flight in three ranks with three paces between the ranks. (3 ranks). This affords space for inspections to be carried out.
OPEN ORDER:	Flight in two ranks, with four paces between ranks. (2 ranks)
PIVOT FLANK:	The flank on which a unit pivots when changing direction.
PIVOT GUIDE:	The guide on a pivot flank of a unit.
QUARTER GUARD:	A small ceremonial guard, that may be mounted at the main entrance to a unit to pay compliments as required. Not to be confused with a Guard of HONOR. Guard consists of 1 officer, 1 SNCO plus 6 other corporals and cadets. They form up in two ranks.
REVIEW:	A ceremonial parade formed to honor a particular person.
SQUAD:	Small body of cadets formed as working party etc.
SQUADRON:	A unit of two or more flights (subunits), Approximately same size as Army/Navy company.
SUPER-NUMERARY:	Extra ranks formed behind rear rank of unit, comprising of officers and SNCO's.
TO CANT:	To incline or tilt an object.
TO DRESS:	To adjust and take up the correct alignment.
WHEELING:	A drill movement by which a body of cadets bring forward a flank on a fixed or moving pivot.
WING:	Formation consisting of two or more squadrons or units. (approx same size as Army Battalion or Navy Division).

COMMAND		TIME/PACE	WHEN EXECUTIVE COMMAND IS GIVEN
TURNINGS and INCLINES			
"About"	- "TURN"	Quick	As the LEFT HEEL strikes the ground.
"About"	- "TURN"	Slow	As the LEFT FOOT is on the ground.
"Right"	- "TURN"	Quick	As the LEFT HEEL strikes the ground.
"Right"	- "TURN"	Slow	As the LEFT FOOT is on the ground.
"Right"	- "INCLINE"	Quick	As the LEFT HEEL strikes the ground.
"Right"	- "INCLINE"	Slow	As the LEFT FOOT is on the ground.
"Left"	- "TURN"	Quick	As the RIGHT HEEL strikes the ground.
"Left"	- "TURN"	Slow	As the RIGHT FOOT is on the ground
"Left"	- "INCLINE"	Quick	As the RIGHT HEEL strikes the ground.
"Left"	- "INCLINE"	Slow	As the RIGHT FOOT is on the ground.
HALTING			
"HALT"		Double Time	As the LEFT FOOT strikes the ground.
"HALT"		Quick Time	As the LEFT HEEL strikes the ground.
"HALT"		Slow Time	As the RIGHT FOOT is on the ground.
"HALT"		Mark Time	As the LEFT FOOT strikes the ground.
COMPLIMENTS			
"Eyes" - "LEFT/RIGHT/ FRONT"		Quick	As the LEFT HEEL strikes the ground
"Eyes" - "LEFT/RIGHT/ FRONT"		Slow	As the RIGHT FOOT is on the ground.
To "LEFT/RIGHT/ FRONT" "SALUTE"		Quick	As the LEFT HEEL strikes the ground.
To "LEFT/RIGHT/ FRONT" "SALUTE"		Slow	As the LEFT FOOT is on the ground.

COMMAND	TIME/PACE	WHEN EXECUTIVE COMMAND IS GIVEN
"Step - "OUT/SHORT"	- Slow & Quick	As the LEFT HEEL strikes the ground.

MARCHING

"Change" -"STEP"	- Quick	As the RIGHT HEEL strikes the ground.
"Change" -"STEP"	- Slow	As the RIGHT FOOT is on the ground.
"Quick" - "March"	- From Slow	As the LEFT HEEL strikes the ground.
"Slow" - "March"	- From Quick	As the LEFT HEEL strikes the ground.
"Break into slow time" "SLOW MARCH"	- From Quick Time	As the LEFT HEEL strikes the ground.

MARKING TIME

"Mark" -"TIME" -	- Breaking into Quick time	As the LEFT FOOT is on the ground.
"Mark" -"TIME"	- Breaking into - Slow time	As the RIGHT FOOT Strikes the ground.
"Change" -"STEP"	- Quick	As the RIGHT HEEL strikes the ground.
"Change" -"STEP"	- Slow	As the RIGHT FOOT is on the ground.
"Mark" - "TIME"	- Slow & Quick	As the LEFT HEEL (When Marching) strikes the ground.
"For" - "WARD"	- Quick	As the LEFT FOOT (When Marking Time) strikes the ground.

MOVING OFF WITH A PRECEDING UNIT

"Quick" - "MARCH"	- Quick	As their RIGHT HEELS strike the ground.
"Slow" - "MARCH"	- Slow	As their RIGHT FEET strike the ground.

USEFUL INFORMATION ON DRILL

Length of Paces in Marching.

Slow March	75cm (30inches)
Quick March	75cm (30inches)
March Sideways	30cm (12inches) " x Paces"

"Left" or "Right Close" -"MARCH"

Maximum number of five paces.

Stepping Short	53cms (21inches)
Stepping Out	83cms (33inches)
Stepping Forward/Backward	75cms (30inches)

" X Paces" "Forward/Backward" "MARCH".

Maximum number of five paces.

PACES/TIME IN MARCHING

Slow March	65 Paces per minute.
Quick March	116 " " "
Sideways Marching and	116 " " "
Stepping Forward or Backward	

ADJUSTING ON PARADE

The term `Adjusting' on parade, is when you feel that your boot lace has come undone, or your shirt is coming out of your trousers or even worse is left to your imagination, but you must put it right before some disaster happens.

So you ADJUST ON PARADE as explained below:-
Place your RIGHT FOOT 12 inches to the rear, make the required adjustment and return to your previous position.
Should you be carrying a Rifle - GROUND ARMS first.
If you are stood AT EASE, always come to ATTENTION before carrying out the ADJUSTMENT drill.

SIZING A SQUAD

This is a simple method of sorting out the different heights of cadets in a flight or squadron so as they appear more uniform when seen as a marching body.

This is especially important if you have some very small and very tall Cadets in the flight or squadron as they would look most odd marching next to each other.

You have all the cadets form a single rank with the tallest at one end and the shortest at the other. The words of command are as follows:-

1. "Tallest on the RIGHT, shortest on the LEFT, in single rank" - "SIZE"
   (Cadets quickly sort themselves out to form the single rank)

2. "Squad" - "NUMBER" Starting with the RIGHT HAND cadet who shouts out "ONE", followed by the next who shouts "TWO" and this follows down the file until all have numbered themselves.

3. "Odd numbers, two paces forward" - "MARCH". Even numbers stand still.

4. "Number one stand fast" "Ranks RIGHT and LEFT" - "TURN". The front rank formed by the ODD NUMBERS turn to their RIGHT. The rear rank formed by the EVEN numbers turn to their LEFT.

5. "Form Flight" - "Quick" - "MARCH". The leading cadet of the REAR file wheels to the right followed by the remainder joining the end of the front file.

As this is taking place the first two cadets of the front file march to the rear of number one, turn to the front, take up a position covering off number one. The remainder of the cadets continue to fill the Front, Centre and Rear Ranks in that order, until the squad is formed.

INSPECTION OF A SQUADRON/FLIGHT

To make room between the ranks all inspections are carried out at the Open Order.

Each Rank is stood to attention while being inspected, while those who are waiting or who have been inspected are Stood At Ease.

The Words of Command that you will be given are as follows:-

1. "Squad"- "Squad" -"SHUN".

2. "Open Order" - "MARCH", "Right" - "DRESS", "Eyes" - "FRONT".

3. "Centre and Rear Ranks, Stand At" - "EASE".

4. "Centre Rank "SHUN", "Front Rank",

    "Stand at" - "EASE".

5. "Rear Rank "SHUN", "Centre Rank",

    "Stand At" - "EASE".

6. "Rear Rank, stand at" "EASE", "Flight - SHUN"

7. At the end of the inspection ask permission from the inspecting officer to fall out.

8. "Squad"- "Squad"-"Shun" - Officer on parade - "Fall Out".

MARCHING AND DRESSING OFF

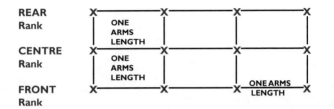

ABOVE DIAGRAM REPRESENTS A SQUAD CORRECTLY DRESSED AND
COVERED OFF FROM LEFT TO RIGHT,
AND FROM FRONT RANK TO REAR

CHANGING DIRECTION - WHEELING ON THE MARCH

Right Hand Cadet Centre and Left Hand of Leading File Cadets lengthening
Turns through their pace. (90°)

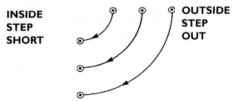

The term "Step Short" means reduce the length of your pace, "Step out"
means slightly lengthen your pace.

By doing this while Wheeling you keep your Dressing in each file as it changes
direction.

A common fault when giving the "Left or Right Wheel" is for the command to
be given sharply, when in fact it should be drawn out - "WHEE-EEL", allowing
the files to slowly change direction, keeping their dressing in threes.

WORDS OF COMMAND

The information below is perhaps the most important for you to learn and practice, as it is only when you are able to correctly give yourself these words of command that you will become good at drill.

The commands given are for when you are "on the march" or "marking time". Like many skills it is only with practice that you will become perfect.

All words of command must be clear and powerful since the way in which they are given affects the reaction that they inspire. The word of command is divided into three parts:

a. **Introductory.** This tells the squad what movements they are about to carry out ie *"Into Line"*.
b. **Cautionary.** The drawn out and loud reminder to the squad ie *"Right"*.
c. **Executive.** The high-pitched, sharp command ie *"Turn"*.

Sometimes there is no need for an introductory word of command ie *"Forward"*. The following are examples of the delivery of a word of command:

Introductory	**C**autionary	**E**xecutive
Voice	*Voice*	*Voice*
Informative, clear and level	Drawn out, loud and falling	Sudden, sharp and loud

Example 1
| **"Into Line"** | **"Right"** | **"Turn"** |

Example 2
| No introductory command | **"Flight"** | **"Halt"** |

DEVELOPING YOUR WORD OF COMMAND

The following information will help you develop good voice control.
Practice whenever you can.

Explanation: *Many drill instructors end up with sore throats after a prolonged drill practice.*
This may well be because they do not use their lungs correctly.

It is important to breathe in through your nose and take your breath 'right down to your stomach'. In other words, learn to breathe deeply. When giving a word of command, 'push' the air out.
Do not forget to stand to attention when giving commands. Standing with your feet apart or leaning backwards may result in straining your groin. KEEP YOUR WEIGHT FORWARD AND YOUR FEET TOGETHER.
Have your head up, looking directly at your squad; when giving the word of command AIM your voice straight over the squad.

Giving Words of Command
Giving a Cautionary or preliminary word of Command you have to pitch your voice on the same note to ensure that it does not 'tail away' at the end. It must be short and sharp. Then comes the Executive word of command, equally short and sharp, "SHUN".
It is most important to develop the correct method of delivering commands; nothing is worse than a poor drill instructor. If you really cannot do it properly, leave it to someone who can.

Words of Command
They must be pronounced CLEARLY. It is not just a sound. A quick tightening of the stomach muscles so that the word comes out quick, a lower pitch to give the **Introductory,** short and higher in pitch than the **Cautionary** produces the **Executive** word of command.(remember **ICE**).
Ensure that there is a pause between the **Cautionary** and the **Executive**. Failure to do this may result in the flight anticipating the word of command, thus the whole purpose of drill is lost - and chaos will reign!
Note: Use your mouth; the wider open it is, the louder the sound!

I	Introductory		**C**	Clear
C	Cautionary		**L**	Loud
E	Executive		**A**	As an order
			P	With Pauses

Drill Instructors Qualities

Drill is exacting and to teach it successfully the instructor must have the following qualities:

a. Patience – never lose your temper.
b. Enthusiasm – you must inspire your squad with a will to learn.
c. Consistent Attitude – set the standard and do not deviate from it.
d. Humanity – understand the squad's problems. Praise readily but do not become familiar, and never humiliate individual members of the squad.
e. Strength of Personality – as a drill instructor you must impress the squad with your personality and always control them fully.
   Example; Recruits imitate their instructors and it is by example that they will learn most.

So you must:

a. When drilling a squad, stand at Attention.
b. When moving, march as you would wish your squad to march.
c. When demonstrating, do so accurately and if the movement is with a rifle, use a rifle and nothing else.
d. Do not use foul or abusive language.
e. Be impeccably turned out.
f. Never exaggerate a movement of drill.

Sequence of Instructing Drill

The following sequence is to be used:

a. Form the Squad.
b. Explanation.
c. Demonstration.
d. Questions.
e. Practice, which should be collective, then individual and collective again

Formation of a Squad: Keep in mind 2 issues:

a. Consider the comfort of the squad. Make sure that they are not looking into the sun or are unnecessarily exposed to the elements.

b. Consider the formation in which they will learn most quickly. The following is a guide:

Use	Formation
Foot Drill:	Straight Line/Hollow Square
Rifle Exercise:	Half Circle
Saluting at the Halt:	Three Ranks, Open Order, Inclined to the Right

Explanation: Explain what you are about to teach and why it is necessary. Demonstration. Broken down as follows:

a. Complete demonstration, calling out the words of command.

b. Demonstration by numbers, pointing out important details.

c. Another complete demonstration.

Questions: After giving the first demonstration by numbers, ask the squad if they have any questions and do so after each subsequent demonstration by numbers.

Practice: After each demonstration by numbers, practise the squad in that movement, checking for faults. Finally, after demonstrating the whole movement, practise the squad judging the time.

DRILL TECHNIQUES TO AID INSTRUCTION

To achieve common standards of drill instruction in the Royal Air Force the following instructional techniques are to be used:

a. **Regulation Pause:** The regulation pause is equal to 2 beats in Quick Time.

When spoken in the course of instruction this pause is represented by the words **"LEFT RIGHT"**.

b. **Movements**: Parts of a drill movement are to be represented by the word **"ONE"**

SAFETY

Before each lesson or drill practice normal safety precautions (NSPs) are to be carried out on rifles. Due regard is to be given to the safe handling of bayonets.

AIDS TO DRILL INSTRUCTION

1. Calling out the Time. Personnel in the early stages of training should call out the time until considered proficient. They must learn to be still when calling out "**LEFT RIGHT**" for the regulation pause. Calling out the time will enable:

   a. Every member of a squad to implement the regulation pause.

   b. The squad to learn to act together.

2. **Time and Pace:** Page 5-14 of this chapter contains the lengths of pace, rates of marching and timings of movements.

3. **Mechanical Aids:** There are three aids the instructor may use to help obtain accurate and smart drill. They are as follows:

   a. The Pace Stick. The Pace Stick is used to gauge the correct length of pace and to measure the distance between ranks. It is a difficult instrument to wield and perfection in the art of turning it, requires constant practice. The instructor should march beside the leading person of the squad, with the stick open and turning to control the length of pace. The instructor should periodically check the length of pace by marching behind the squad with the Pace Stick open and turning (only carried by authorsied Drill Instructor by the Adult Training Facility)

   b. The Metronome: This gives an accurate check on the rate of marching and on the timing of rifle exercises. It can be set to any number of beats per-minute and should be used frequently to maintain uniformity of instruction with regard to timings.

   The electronic metronome with an LCD readout is replacing the swinging arm version.

The Drum: When foot drill and rifle exercises are being taught by numbers at the halt, a drummer may be used by the instructor to provide the cue for a movement.

Three scenarios are as follows:
(1) The drummer is stationed behind the squad and will judge the regulation pause between the cautionary word of command and the drum-tap.
The squad will react more sharply to the tap of the drum than they would to the instructor's word of command.
(2) When foot exercises are being done at the halt whilst judging the time, station a drummer to the rear of the squad. The drummer should have a metronome (set at 40) and should be far enough behind the squad for them not to hear the tick of the metronome.
The drummer will judge the regulation pause between the command and his first tap, if this is possible. Thereafter he will tap the drum on every beat of the metronome for the same number of times as there are movements.

(3) To beat the rate of marching, set the metronome to the rate required. The drummer now beats in time with the metronome and the squad stands still and listens. When the instructor is ready to practise his squad he must have the drummer beating the time to the metronome and then give:

"QUICK MARCH"

To summaries:
Remember: Introductory, **C**autionary, **E**xecutive - **ICE**
Power: Plenty of air into the lungs.
Pitch: Hold your head high and pitch the word of command high
over the Squad.
Punch: Given quickly by tightening the stomach muscles.

Pronunciation: Make your words CLEAR, LOUD, AS AN ORDER.

COMMUNICATION DRILL

This Drill introduces an element of 'fun' into a Drill Lesson. It gives the
individual Cadet the opportunity to use their voice as never before as they
are competing with each other to make themselves heard above the rest of
the Squad.

1. First demonstrate to the squad all words of command at the halt,
   including rifle drill if taught.
2. Then "conduct" the squad while they give elementary words of command;
   insisting on clarity and power from each cadet.
3. Divide the squad in to two ranks, place them about 25 meters apart, with
   5 paces interval between each cadet.
4. Each cadet should now drill his/her opposite number 25 meters away
   without regard to those to the left or right of them.
5. After no more than ten minutes, change the ranks, so that the cadets in
   both ranks have a chance of controlling their opposite number.

MUTUAL DRILL

Form the squad into three ranks and explain the introductory word
of command and which are the DIRECTING FLANK.
Call out each member of the squad in turn to drill the squad and then
call out another member of the squad to watch and be prepared to
comment on his/her performance.
Note:
1. Be patient and make encouraging comments.
2. When correcting, be sure you address your remarks to the whole
   squad, they can all learn by one cadet's mistakes.
Testing you wits
'Ogrady' is a game practiced to sharpen your response to an order.
If the instructor precedes an order with "OGRADY SAYS" then you carry it
out, if not, any who move are 'knocked out" the last Cadet is the winner.

BADGES OF RANK & DISTINGUISHING BADGES

Offices

Cap Badge

Officer RAF VR(T)

Officer Cadet Slider

Pilot Officer Slider

Flight Officer Slider

Beret Badge

Flight Lt. Slider

Sqn Ldr Slider

Wing Cmd Slider

Gp Capt Slider

Warrant Officers & SNCO

Senior NCO Cap Badge

Distinguishing Badge

No 1 Dress

No 2 Dress

Sergeant (ATC)

No 1 Dress

No 2 Dress

Flight Sergeant (ATC)

Cap Badge

Beret Badge

No 1 Dress   No 2 Dress

Warrent Officer (ATC)

No 1 Dress   No 2 Dress

Warrent Officer (ATC)

EX WO 1's only who held a Royal Warrant of the 3 Regular Forces and a number of WO (ATC) holding key posts authorised by Comdt AC only.

BADGES OF RANK & DISTINGUISHING BADGES

Civilian

 ATC Lapel Badge

 Civilian Instructors Lapel Badge

 Chaplains's Scarf Badge

Civilian Instructors Arm Band

Flying

Cadet Pilot

Cadet Pilot Navigator

Glider Instructor

Glider Pilot

Blue Wings

Silver Wings

Gold Wings

BADGES OF RANK & DISTINGUISHING BADGES

Cadets NCO Ranks - 18 years old +

Cadet Warrent Officer

Cadet Flight Sergeant

Cadet Sergeant

Staff Cadet Lanyard

Cadet Corporal

Cadet Lance Corporal CCF Only

Cadet NCO Ranks - 13-17 years old

Cadet Warrent Officer

Cadet Flight Sergeant

Cadet Sergeant

Cadet Corporal

Cadet Lance Corporal CCF Only

Squadron ID Badge

Distinguishing Badge   Distinguishing Badge CCF

Master Air Cadet ATC only

Senior Cadet

Leading Cadet

First Class Cadet

BADGES OF RANK & DISTINGUISHING BADGES

Marksmanship

Squadron Marksman

Wing Marksman

Regional Marksman

Corps Marksman

NRA Cadet 50

NRA Cadet 100

Band -

Drummer

Bandsman

Trumpeter

Instrumentalist

Piper

Drum Major

Bandmaster

Gold Badges - *Air Cadet National Bands (Marching, Concert, Pipe)* - **Silver Badges** *Sqn, Wing, Region Bands*

BADGES OF RANK & DISTINGUISHING BADGES

Specialist

Duke of Edinburghs Awards

Bronze Award

Silver Award

Gold Award

First Aid Awards

Youth First Aid award

Adult First award

Air Cadet Leadership Awards

Lord Lieutenants
Cadet award

Air Cadet
Leadership award

Nijmegen March
award

Communications
award

BADGES OF RANK & DISTINGUISHING BADGES

Brassard Badge Positioning

Air Cadets

Combined Cadet Force

Please consult your unit adult instructors, to find out the correct position of badge on your brassard, these images above are examples only.

SELF TEST QUESTIONS

1. What is Saluting in recognition of.
2. What is a squad in "Close Order".
3. What would you be doing correctly "the longest way up and shortest down".
4. If a squad of 20 cadet are marching on a road, what formation would they be in.
5. How do you dry out your leather boots.
6. Up to how many cadets would be in a Guard of Honor.
7. The pocket of your uniform must not be what...
8. How should your Beret band be on your forehead.
9. On what foot is the HALT given.
10. Marking Time, when is the HALT given.
11. What is a Quarter Guard.
12. What does the drill term "To Dress" mean.
13. What do you understand by an "INTRODUCTORY" word of command.
14. What sort of socks should you wear with boots.
15. When do you "Step Short" and "Step Out"
18. At Close Order what is the distance between ranks.
16. Marking Time, the HALT is given when the knee is ...
17. What and who are Supernumeraries.
18. Why do you have Preliminary and Executive words of command.
19. What is the difference between an "Incline" and a "Turn".
20. How many pace can you "Sideways March".
21. How many paces per minute is the Quick March.
22. What do you understand by "Adjusting" on parade.
23. How do you "SIZE" a squad and why.
24. Before a squad is inspected, what has to be done before it started.

in his Spitfire DAZ, shoot down 14 enemy aircraft.

Chapter 4

SHOOTING IN THE AIR CADETS

Service shooting is split into two distinct activities; Shooting as a Sport or Competition Shooting and Qualification/Operational Firing.

It is very difficult to try and treat them separately when you get down to the serious business of the skills required for shooting.

However as a member of the Cadet Forces Competitive Shooting is what you will be doing.

Many of the shooting principles generally apply equally to both Shooting as a Sport and Qualification/Operational Firing.

The basic skills required are very much the same, but applied for a different purpose, we make no apologies about this, just ask you to bear it in mind throughout this Chapter.

We need to stress that there is NOT an unrestricted supply of ammunition, and point out that it is just as much credit for you to be a Marksman with an Air Weapon as it is with the GP Rifle, L98A2 Target Rifle or the 5.56 Rifle, in maintaining your skill as a marksman.

What is important is for everyone to make good use of what range allocations and ammunition you do have available; for as many as possible to have the chance to take part in shooting on a regular basis.

The administration to organise a Range for you to shoot and to get a date allocated, means that your full support is required on the day to ensure the facilities are fully used by as many as possible.

At the time this Pocket Book is being written, there are many anti-shooting organisations, whose intentions are to stop shooting make it so difficult that those who are interested will give it up. They are paying particular attention to young people who use Shooting as a hobby or who are members of the Cadet Forces. It requires you to pay special attention to the Rules and Safety Regulations.

BUILD YOUR CONFIDENCE

We know from our Cadet experience that shooting is well controlled and supervised. You can play your part by just being a good shot and a member of your Detachment Shooting Team.

Hopefully, this Skill at Arms Chapter dealing with shooting will help you to:-

1. Think positively about your training and what you could do personally to improve it.
2. Give you information and ideas for you to apply in your own training.
3. Maintain a steady improvement in your results, giving you more confidence in your ability.
4. Gain your interest in pursuit of better results making you a better team member.
5. To pass on your skills to others who may be just starting to shoot.
6. Respect the patience and interest your Instructors and Coaches have given to train you, and meet their expectations of you in return.

Once you start to improve - nothing will hold you back - only you can make the choice.

Don't miss a chance to have a practice shoot, no matter what type of weapon or range -

PRACTICE MAKES PERFECT.

PAST EXPERIENCE

Should you live in a town or city it is most likely that your first experience of shooting was at a Shooting Gallery at a fair or in an amusement arcade. If you were very lucky you might have walked away with a useless prize, such as a plastic duck or a bag of marbles! Your ability to shoot accurately had very little to do with your skill. The weapons used in these places are not meant to be too accurate as they would have to give away too many prizes and as a result - not make any profit.!!

SHOOTING IN THE COUNTRYSIDE

Those of you who are fortunate enough to live in the country or who are able to 'get out' into our beautiful countryside, may have the opportunity to use a shot gun or rifle in the pursuit of sport. Some of you will live in parts of the country where the wildlife in large areas of the countryside is preserved and carefully looked after by Game Keepers. Many of their working days are spent with either a shot gun or rifle in their hands. The 'prizes' they win for their shooting could be the fox that kill some of their Pheasants.

CONSERVATION AND PRESERVATION

The shepherd on the hills and in the dales has to be a good shot with a rifle to protect his sheep from predators, such as foxes or stray dogs who are not kept under control by their owners or fancies a bit of lamb for its dinner.

The opportunity to spend time with people in the countryside whose living depends on using a gun, should not be missed. You may not like the idea of seeing some of our wildlife being shot and killed in the pursuit of sport or in the course of controlling vermin, but if you leave that aspect to one side and look at the skills required to be a good shot, and the fact that if you were a gamekeeper or shepherd and NOT a good shot, you would cause a great deal of unnecessary suffering by wounding an animal and it escaping to die a lingering death.

DUKE OF EDINBURGH AWARD SCHEME AND SHOOTING

Shooting is one of the pursuits recognised for participation in the Duke of Edinburgh Award Scheme and therefore your time and effort spent in becoming a good shot can be rewarded through the scheme.

JOIN THE TEAM

Some Wings/Regions are very keen on shooting and have regular annual rifle meetings at which there is a great competitive spirit, and out of these events many of their teams for Bisley are selected for special training. This is where you have the opportunity to come to the notice of your Wing/Region Shooting Officer, when you are consistent good shot, showing all the signs of being able to apply that ability, also having the right temperament, interest, application etc., to warrant further training as a member of your Squadron or School 'Shooting Team'. You must bear in mind all that we have said about your ability not only to consistently shoot well, but to work as a valued member of a team. Safety is very important at all times especially when carrying out Skill at Arms Training, but firing live ammunition on a Rifle Range gives SAFETY a more immediate importance. There are strict Range Safety Rules that will be read to you every time you go on the Range.

TYPES OF SHOOTING ACTIVITY

When you consider the shooting we do within the Cadet Forces it takes on a different meaning to that of the Armed Services.

The reason does not need explaining other than the role of the services and their needs in terms of Skill at Arms using small calibre weapons are more complicated than ours, and of course serve a totally different purpose. You must also remember that a soldiers pay and promotion prospects are linked to their skills, efficiency and fitness.

As already mentioned within the Armed Services there are essentially two distinct "Shooting Activities" which can be split into Competition Shooting and Qualification/Operational Firing.

It is very difficult to try and treat them separately when you get into the serious business of shooting.

The reason is that many of the shooting principles generally apply equally to both Competition Shooting and Qualification/Operational Firing, because of this you may sometimes feel that they are both mixed up together, the skills required are very much the same, but applied for a different purpose.

COMPETITIVE SHOOTING

Shooting in the Cadet Forces comes under the umbrella of Competitive Shooting. This not only applies to the Shooting Practices for your proficiency marksman qualifications, but also for many Wing/Region and National competitions, having a variety of conditions that make them interesting and challenging to both the individual and team competitors.

Details of these competitions are to be found from pages 98 onwards under "Competitive Shooting".

Get your unit OC to enter a team for some of the events, you will all enjoy it, particularly if you are fit and have stamina.

Every year there is the Cadet Rifle Meeting at Bisley. Many hundreds of cadets from the UK and Commonwealth Cadet Forces take part in the various competitions. You could be one of those competitors and/or a member of your Wing/Region shooting team. It is a great experience to be there and see how keen the competitive spirit is between those taking part.

SKILL AT ARMS AND SHOOTING

We must also consider Skill at Arms and Shooting in relation to the current syllabus of training for the ATO and the Combined Cadet Force.

You need to understand of the role of Operational Firing and most certainly many of the subjects related to it Vis,. Training Tests, Fire Control Orders, Types of Fire, Section Leading, Patrols etc., but, it must be stressed that this does not actually involve Operational Firing.

BE A MARKSMAN WITH EVERY WEAPON

Like the Armed Services, the Cadet Forces do not have an un-limited supply of ammunication. You are likely to have the opportunity to spend far more time firing an Air Rifle as the ranges are more readily available and the 'ammunition' (pellets) not so expensive. Provided Air Rifles are properly cared for they can be very accurate, but you will still need to put in a lot of practice to become a Marksman.

There is something rather special about learning how to use a weapon safely and correctly, to take care of it and learn how to fire it producing good results. Don't think for one moment that it's one of those "MACHO" activities that seems to be the 'in-thing' to have a go at. It is a challenge to you as a Cadet to have the ability, stamina and patience to develop the required skills. In due course you may become a Marksman with one of the types of weapon you fire, if you try hard enough you should master all of them and be awarded your marksman badges.

GO SHOOTING REGULARLY

It is important for everyone to make good use of what range allocations and ammunition we have made available to us, and for as many as possible to have the chance to take part in shooting on a regularly.

It follows that when your OC has arranged a shooting practice he/she will expect you to be there, not just to shoot, but to help run the range and to encourage others to do better.

Skill at Arms Training will introduce you to the weapons fired in the Cadet Force. The Skill at Arms sections in your Pocket Book will help you towards the knowledge and skills required, but there is nothing like practice to make perfect.

SHOOTING WITH THE RESERVER FORCES

Your cadet unit/school should have close liaison with the local Reserve Forces units & local military establishments and through this contact a great deal of shooting practice can be arranged.

Not that you would expect to fire ALL the weapons they use nor the practises they run, but it is another opportunity for you to practice and also makes good competition. Your contribution to time on the open ranges will no doubt be to help them by assisting in the Butts, signalling and marking up targets. You may get lucky and use an Electric Target Range (ETR), or SARTS range (Small Arms Range Targetry System) or DCCT (Dismounted Combat Trainer) when there is no marking to be done. Perhaps the greatest difference between 'Shooting as a Sport' and 'Qualifying/Operational Firing' is that a soldier has to be very fit to carry out 'Qualifying/Operational firing' practices, as many of them involve practices running down the range or tactical firing on ETR ranges or Close Quarter Battle Ranges (CQBR).

PRACTISE MAKE PERFECT

If you are already keen on shooting in particular, you need to work hard advantage of every opportunity to spend time firing on the range.

There is always room for improvement. You must strive to improve your performance, knowing that the enjoyment will be the reward of being a good shot.

To a Recruit - a word of warning - do not be put-off if at first you don't get a reasonable result; just remember if at first you don't succeed -try, try again. You must stick at it, as it is necessary in shooting. Your score suffers directly by the errors you make; there is no second chance. If you make less mistakes than the others - you will win.

PERSONAL QUALITIES

It is within the ability of almost anyone to become a good shot, provided they are 'mentally' and 'physically' fit.

Mental Fitness - because it is to a great extent the 'mental control' that is required once you have learned the skills needed. The determination and keenness to succeed relies on Mental Fitness.

Physical Fitness in this context is the need to have those parts of the body working sufficiently well to hold, sight and fire the weapon accurately, and to re-load - if it's not a self loading weapon!

Many firers on the range find out for the first time that their eyesight is not as good as they imagined it was. Even as young as you are , have your eyesight checked at regular intervals.

On the plus side, shooting is a great sport and gives you fun and satisfaction. It does repay you for all the time and effort you have given to arrive at producing good results.

SAFE AND SKILLED

You will have been taught how to handle the weapon SAFELY and master the basic skills by your instructors.

Once you are qualified in these basic skills, then you will start to be given training in some depth by coaching you for marksmanship during live firing practices. Your 'coach' will modify the basic techniques to suit your individual needs.

GOING ON THE RANGE

Having arrived on the Range and moved to the area of the Firing Point in preparation for your shooting, the most important action that must be carried out are the Range Safety Drills.

These and other Range Standing Orders will be explained to you by the Range Officer, who is responsible for Range Discipline and the safety of those on or in the vicinity of the Range.

PERSONAL HEALTH/SAFETY

You are at all times responsible for your own safety, not to do anything that will constitute a danger to yourself or others. The noise of weapons being fired can damage your hearing - UNLESS YOU TAKE PRECAUTIONS by wearing some form of protection.

You must wear EAR DEFENDERS at all times when firing a weapon. Do not take part in shooting practices without them.

NOTE: *check your ear defenders particularly if there are cracks in the plastic around the ear cup or if the foam sound protection is missing from within the ear cup.*

PERSONNEL INSPECTION

You will be inspected - your pockets and all personal equipment, webbing etc, will be checked to make sure that no DRILL ROUNDS are brought onto the Range.

When you have finished on the range and just before you leave, you will be inspected again, this time for any live rounds of ammunition or empty cases. It is very easy to have missed a loose round in the bottom of your webbing equipment, but now is the time that you must be sure that you have none. Should you find any, don't try and hide them, give them to the Range Officer or the Instructor when they inspect you as set out in your Personal Declaration AS SET OUT BELOW.

YOUR PERSONAL DECLARATION

At the actual time of your inspection by the Range Officer or Instructor you will make a declaration (tell them) as they come to you by saying:-

These and other Range Rules apply equally to all personnel on the Range, you will see your instructors and officers inspect each other in your presence.

MARKSMANSHIP PRINCIPLES

The Definition of a Good Shot - What is Essential?

"To fire a shot without it disturbing your aim"

To achieve this:-

1. Your FIRING POSITION and the HOLD must be FIRM ENOUGH to SUPPORT the weapon.
2. The weapon must point naturally in the direction of the target, without any undue physical effort.
3. The alignment of your sights and aiming must be correct.
4. You control the rhythm of your breathing and operate the trigger correctly.
5. The shot will be fired and 'followed through' without undue movement disturbing your aim."

You must learn these Marksmanship Principles, until they become firmly established in your mind.

The application of them demands great concentration on your part, this combined with the determination to be a Marksman will ensure success.

LYING POSITION and HOLDING

You must develop the control you have over HOLDING the weapon, to keep it steady. This is the foundation upon which to carry out the other activities, Vis **BREATHING, AIMING, TRIGGER OPERATION, FOLLOW THROUGH.**

Only when you have mastered the correct HOLDING will you start to improve upon your results. **GET THE BASICS RIGHT - FIRST.**

The Lying Postion

The lying position is the basic shooting position as it gives the firer the best support for the weapon, it is least tiring and presents the smallest image as a target to the enemy.

To maintain steadiness and be able to achieve a perfect hold, the first essential is that you are comfortable and feel that your weapon is a part of you.

The importance of this cannot be over emphasised.

Position on The Ground

The position to be adopted on the ground, is with your body slightly oblique to the line of fire from which you are able to achieve the CORRECT AIM in the shortest time.

When getting on the ground hold the PISTOL GRIP with the Right hand, lie down, breaking your fall with the LEFT hand, keep the weapon parallel to the ground, make sure that no dirt gets into the MUZZLE.

When you are down on the ground, tilt the weapon to the right, and support it by placing your LEFT hand under the HAND GUARD across the palm of your hand and hold with your fingers together. The grip should be no more than a stable platform for the weapon. NO attempt should be made to grip the HAND GUARD tightly or pull it backwards into the shoulder. **The position should be one of support.**

The LEFT elbow is positioned as close as possible - in a comfortable position - to a point directly below the weapon. This position is intended to support the weight of the weapon on the bone of the arm, rather than using your muscular effort to support and hold the weapon, which could not be sustained for very long.

You must be aware that this may produce a 'strained' position which is nt comfortable for you, if so, you will not produce your best results, therefore adopt a comfortable position within the constraints of the correct hold.

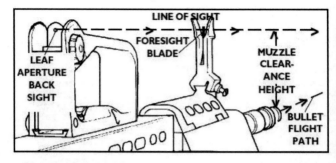

GET COMFORTABLE

The BUTT should be in a position against the muscle between the shoulder joint and the lower edge of your collar bone - it should not come into contact with the bone itself.

Your RIGHT hand is the controlling hand and is the most important factor in good shooting. It should be high up on the PISTOL GRIP, with the web of the skin between thumb and forefinger positioned at the back of the PISTOL GRIP.

The grip must be firm, pulling back into the shoulder, but take care NOT to twist the weapon causing the SIGHTS not to be upright.

The first joint of your forefinger should be naturally on the TRIGGER. The position of the RIGHT ELBOW is determined after taking the correct grip with your hand on the PISTOL GRIP.

Your elbow also helps to keep your right shoulder in the correct position all the time.

Your body should be slightly at a angle to the 'line of fire', and your muscles in a relaxed state.

As you may not be accustomed to regular visits to the range, you may find it difficult to relax as there is always a certain amount of excitement in shooting. However in spite of this it is a part of the Self Discipline that you will need to master every time you get down to fire,

REMEMBER: BE - COOL - CALM, and COLLECT your THOUGHTS.

Your LEFT leg should be in line with your body, your RIGHT leg is positioned to form a continuation of the line of fire.

Relax your leg muscles and turn your toes outwards with your heels on the ground. This position gives you the maximum amount of contact between your body and the ground, affording you the most comfortable position.

This position often, and quite naturally puts extra pressure on your chest in contact with the ground. This can affect your breathing rhythm and you may feel that it restricts your breathing.

If this is so, bend your right knee and bring your leg up slightly. This will raise the right side of your body just enough to make your breathing easier.

Keep your head in an upright position, this is it's natural position and therefore the instinct to maintain your sense of balance and to correctly position your eyes immediately behind the sights.

Don't press your cheek hard against the CHEEK PIECE of the BUTT. Rest it lightly in a position that is comfortable and that you can keep for the time you are firing a practice.

Don't get your eye too near to the BACK SIGHT. The distance should never be LESS than 25mm away.

AUTOMATIC ALIGNMENT WITH THE TARGET

The Marksmanship Principle - "That requires the rifle to point naturally at the target" needs little explanation as you will know how to adopt the correct firing position, but, if you are in a position that you have to strain even the smallest muscle to achieve the CORRECT AIM PICTURE it can affect your results.

At the moment you fire your weapon it will move against or be affected by that 'small muscle strain'.

This strain is in force at the very moment you fire, in fact before the round leaves the MUZZLE of the weapon, the weapon will move against this strain and as a result your correct aim will be "off" and your results affected.

On firing it cannot be helped that your weapon will move, but natural alignment will go a long way to ensure that the movement is kept to a minimum. Once you have had some experience of firing it will become easier for you to get into a correctly aligned position each time you fire. Until that time arrives you will have to practise 'testing and adjusting' until you find the most 'comfortable position'.

A useful tip to help find a 'comfortable position' is to shut your eyes and come up into the aim. As your eyes are shut you will instinctively adopt the most comfortable stance. On opening your eyes, the AIM PICTURE should be on or very near the POINT OF AIM you had. If not your position should be altered.

ADJUSTING YOUR POSITION - OTHER WAYS

Other ways to adjust your position are as follows:-

Aim at the target and then relax your hold. You should not notice any great change in your aim.

If there is, then it is an indication that you need to adjust your position.

If you need to correct lateral - LEFT to RIGHT errors. Keep your left elbow still, move your body slightly to the LEFT or RIGHT as required.

To correct VERTICAL errors, keep both your elbows still, and lift your body slightly forward or backwards as you require. Keep the BUTT in the same position in your shoulder.

The more you practice, it will become second nature to automatically adopt the correct position without adjustment.

SIGHT ALIGNMENT - AIMING

The CORRECT AIM PICTURE requires several different actions to be carefully co-ordinated at the same time, not just once, but time after time using exactly the same formula on each occasion. It is a lot to ask of our human make up to perform this, that is why you have to practise and have the patience to develop the skill.

To achieve this CORRECT AIM PICTURE you have to align:-

1. Your EYE.
2. The CENTRE of the BACK SIGHT.
3. The CENTRAL POINT of the TIP of the FORESIGHT.
4. Place the sights - so aligned on the point of aim on the target. See the diagram below.

CORRECT SIGHT OF AIM (MILITARY SHOOTING)

POINT
OF
AIM

The correct focusing of your eyesight is essential to carry out the aiming.
It is important to understand that you are asking your eye to focus on two objects at different distances both at the same time. The objects are the TARGET, OR the TIP of the FORESIGHT.

The critical part of SIGHT ALIGNMENT is the connection between the BACK SIGHT APERTURE and the FORESIGHT.

Any errors you make are multiplied in proportion to the range of the target, so it is most important to make sure that the FORESIGHT is in clear focus at the moment of 'SHOT RELEASE'.

The tendency is to focus on the target and in so doing draw your attention away from the connection there should be between the FORESIGHT and the APERTURE BACK SIGHT.

With sufficient practise and experience your eye will automatically line up the centre of the APERTURE in the BACK SIGHT, BUT, don't get carried away by thinking this does not need regular practice and concentration - it does!.

FATIGUE WEAKNESS

Should you be involved in a long period of firing there is no doubt that some form of fatigue will become apparent.

Usually you will notice that it is your eyes that become tired, especially if you are inclined to remain in the aim too long.

As your eye gets tired its power of clear vision rapidly reduces. It can become upsetting if your results become erratic.

To prevent this there has to be an instantaneous movement of your trigger.
(This is not to be confused with a common fault of a nervous firer who -ignoring all that has been taught - may be inclined to close their eyes and 'snatch' the trigger.)

This instantaneous movement should not change the grip you have with your right hand and therefore the immediate action of your trigger finger will not alter your CORRECT AIM.

It is out of the question to take your time over the actual 'operation of the trigger' to actually fire the weapon - YOU DON'T HAVE TIME.

TAKE YOUR TIME

This is when it is important for you to strictly control the amount of time that you allow yourself for firing the number of rounds in each practise.
It is better to take a more leisurely approach, come down off the aim and start again.

While out of the aim, relax and give your eyes a rest. It is always said that to look at the grass near to you on the range is good for the eyes, green being a restful colour.

Don't look down the range or at distant objects as your eyes have been accustomed to being focused on near objects such as your sights, therefore look at objects close by.

Once you are in the aim - discipline yourself to get off your shots in say, the space of SIX seconds - dependent upon your individual skills, preference and the conditions of the practice.

Just give it some careful thought for a moment, consider that no matter how strong and steady your hold may be with your weapon, you cannot physically hold it in that EXACT POSITION for more than a few seconds.

It is the co-ordination of all activities, that when your eye says "CORRECT AIM" the weapon MUST fire. NOT before, or AFTER, it MUST GO ON THE DOT.

CONTROL OF BREATHING

We all breathe naturally at a steady rate with very little change in the rate of the number of breaths we take per minute, it has a natural rhythm - that is UNLESS we do something to upset it and it takes very little to do just that.

Operational Shooting Practises invariably involve running down the range. You will experience that when you are out of breath - no matter how fit you are - that it is more difficult to concentrate on what you are doing. When you come up into the aim, your sights are not in focus, in fact may be blurred. You are far from being steady - never mind getting the right AIM PICTURE.

The reason for this is a lack of oxygen in the blood stream. It must be rapidly replaced by CORRECT BREATHING, which in turn reduces the tension and strain, allowing you to get back to the normal rhythm of breathing in the shortest possible time. You will now appreciate that it is very important to keep your breathing under control when you are shooting.

The need to be "cool - calm - and collected" especially when leading up to the point at which you actually make the decision to fire the shot.

To assist you in this refer to the diagram and the notes on page 89. Practice the timing for "Breathing for Firing" as shown in the illustration until it becomes second nature, then apply it when you are shooting.

Three Stages

There are three stages in the normal breathing cycle that are important to consider when shooting.

a. During normal breathing your lungs are neither completely filled nor emptied.

b. When breathing out there is a natural pause.

c. The time for the whole "cycle" takes about SIX seconds. It is plain to see that the ideal time to fire a shot will be when your body is having a natural pause in the breathing cycle.

The idea is to slightly extend that pause by a couple of seconds, to EIGHT seconds.

BREATHING FOR FIRING

1. Take several SLOW, DEEP BREATHS, giving the oxygen time to be absorbed into your blood stream.
2. Don't empty your lungs, take a slightly larger breath and hold it for about six seconds - see diagram below — "Breath Restraint to Release Shot".
3. During those critical six seconds, you will find the CORRECT AIM and operate the TRIGGER, afterwards, continue to breathe normally.

If for some reason you decide not to fire, relax and start again. REMEMBER: This can only be achieved by the independent movement of the TRIGGER FINGER whilst the remainder of your body is perfectly still.

Eventually co-ordinated control of your breathing and release of the shot will become a reflex action.

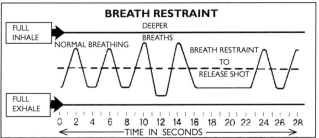

TRIGGER CONTROL & OPERATION

In the early stages of shooting a beginner has to consciously direct their finger to pull the trigger, but with training, this becomes a conditioned reflex action.

Errors in trigger control can lose a firer many points, especially at short range.

TRIGGERS

There are two basic types of trigger you may come across in shooting, a TWO STAGE (normally found in military rifles) and a SINGLE STAGE usually fitted on small-bore rifles, but in recent time more are now being fitted to full-bore rifles.

It is important that the grip of the RIGHT hand (LEFT hand for left handed firers) does not interfere with the trigger operation.

The only part of the trigger finger that should be in contact with the rifle should be part which is ON THE TRIGGER. The trigger should operate in the same way each time and go at the same pressure.

With the two stage trigger, the first pressure is taken up while settling into position.

When ready as soon as a clear sight picture is seen, the second pressure is operated, smoothly and quickly in one movement.

With a single stage trigger the operation is the same as for the second stage of a two stage trigger.

THE FOLLOW THROUGH

It is possible that you may respond to TRIGGER action or other influences at the very moment the weapon is fired and the BULLET is still in the BARREL. This can cause a shot to be misplaced, even so, it is essential that the shot is "followed through" to the target. It requires you to concentrate during the period of TRIGGER operation and SHOT RELEASE.

CALLING THE SHOT

It is essential that the firer should be able to "CALL THE SHOT", in other words, be able to predict if a shot has been misplaced and where it may go. On the FOLLOW THROUGH as above if the rifle does not come to rest where expected, the position where it does come to rest can indicate where the shot will have gone. If it comes to rest at a different point each time , the GROUP is likely to be large and other factors will need to be examined e.g. Position, Sling or Hold.

CHARACTERISTICS OF THE WEAPON

Particularly in Competitive shooting, the ability to fire your weapon and for it to produce a "GROUP" of shots within a certain specified maximum area, is the essential requirement for you and your weapon to achieve.

You have to have complete confidence, not only in your own capability, but also your weapons ability to achieve this goal. Once this confidence is achieved the weapon becomes an extension of your body.

TEST YOUR INDIVIDUAL WEAPON

A short range is better to test weapons, 30 or 100 metres - they are not affected by errors due to the wind.

Check that the weapon you are about to use is in fact 'your weapon'. Ensure that the Barrel and CHAMBER are dry cleaned for firing.

Check that the weapon is functioning correctly, and if appropriate, that the magazine is correctly filled.

A Grouping Practice of five or more rounds should then be fired at any type of target having an easily defined Aiming Mark.

Should you make a faulty shot, this should be declared to your coach.

Weapons of the same type often have slight variations when fired, also the weather conditions, wind etc. may have to be taken into consideration as it can effect how your weapon fires.

WHAT SHOOTING COMPETITIONS DOES YOUR CADET UNIT TAKE PART IN ?

With practice under a variety of conditions, you will get to know how your weapon performs and become accustomed to its own characteristics.

This aspect of shooting is especially important when taking part in your early training, but just as important in competitive shooting.

When firing your practices on the range you should have an experienced shot with you as a "Coach", who will be down by your side on the firing point.

COACHING CARD 100 METRES

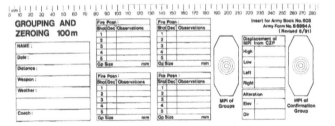

DIAGRAM OF A 4FT TARGET ILLUSTRATING A "GROUP"

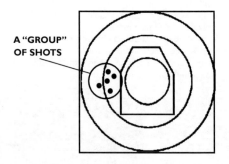

A "GROUP" OF SHOTS

PRODUCING A GOOD "GROUP"

You will read and be constantly told that "your ability to shoot well depends entirely upon being able to GROUP TIGHTLY" or " you must have a good GROUPING capacity".

To explain this, if you imagine that perhaps the ideal method of holding and firing a weapon would be to have it clamped firmly in some device on the firing point - so as it cannot move, load and fire it at a target 100 metres away.

You may not belive it, but a weapon fired under these 'ideal' conditions would not put all the shots through the same hole in the target, it would produce shots spread out in a "GROUP".

It is not suggested that you can hold it as firmly as some device, but to start off with, to be a good shot it is essential to learn to shoot when in the prone or lying position.

In this position the greater part of your body area is in contact with the ground, giving you a stable or firm base from which you can master the techniques and skills that you will be taught.

It will be with constant practice that you will reduce the size of your grouping capacity and at the same time learn how to move your group into the centre of the target.

Remember - practice makes perfect

THE SLING - AN AID TO GOOD SHOOTING

Many of the 'Top Shots' in the world who shoot at Bisley use a sling as a shooting aid. The purpose of using the sling is to give extra support and stability to the weapon you are holding, and to reduce some of the strain or fatigue in supporting the weapon.

This helps to keep the LEFT arm vertical under the weapon and does not exert any sideways pressure. The second - a TWO POINT SLING is secured at the forend and on the BUTT as normal. This is used in a similar manner to the Single Point Sling, with the sling wound over your wrist and round your arm, again with it above your elbow on your upper arm.

SINGLE POINT SLING

For interest only - the illustration on the next page gives a clear picture of how a SINGLE POINT SLING is mostly used in civilian competition TARGET SHOOTING.

A Single Point sling is not usually used in military shooting as the firer uses the sling and fitments which are part of the weapon.

Most shooting teams buy leather slings that are softer material to handle and also wider, which are more comfortable.

CARE AND CLEANING

This subject has already been dealt with in some detail, but it must be emphasised that your CARE and CLEANING when you are involved in competitive shooting must be meticulous.

This extra care of your weapon may reveal something that could put you out of the competition - if you had not found it. It will pay dividends to be extra careful with all aspects of Care and Cleaning.

Proper cleaning will extend the barrel life, careless cleaning can cause damage.

Before the Shoot

1. Clean out the barrel using full length rod, rod guide , jag and flannelette. NEVER pull a dirty patch back up the barrel.
2. Polish the barrel by repeating as above.
3. Dry all metal surfaces, especially the bolt and inside the action.

THE SINGLE POINT SLING

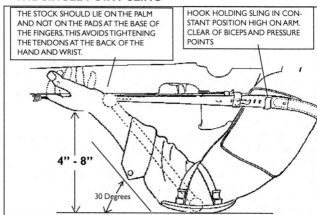

THE STOCK SHOULD LIE ON THE PALM AND NOT ON THE PADS AT THE BASE OF THE FINGERS. THIS AVOIDS TIGHTENING THE TENDONS AT THE BACK OF THE HAND AND WRIST.

HOOK HOLDING SLING IN CONSTANT POSITION HIGH ON ARM. CLEAR OF BICEPS AND PRESSURE POINTS

4" - 8"

30 Degrees

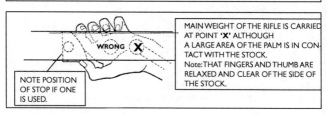

WRONG

NOTE POSITION OF STOP IF ONE IS USED.

MAIN WEIGHT OF THE RIFLE IS CARRIED AT POINT '**X**' ALTHOUGH A LARGE AREA OF THE PALM IS IN CONTACT WITH THE STOCK. Note: THAT FINGERS AND THUMB ARE RELAXED AND CLEAR OF THE SIDE OF THE STOCK.

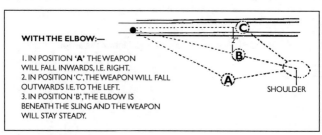

WITH THE ELBOW:—

1. IN POSITION '**A**' THE WEAPON WILL FALL INWARDS, I.E. RIGHT.
2. IN POSITION 'C', THE WEAPON WILL FALL OUTWARDS I.E. TO THE LEFT.
3. IN POSITION 'B', THE ELBOW IS BENEATH THE SLING AND THE WEAPON WILL STAY STEADY.

SHOULDER

2"

TARGETS

The illustrations and information on targets in the following pages are a sample of the many different targets you will come across if you develop a keen interest in shooting.

Please be aware that they are **NOT** to scale and are reproduced to give you a representation of how they appear.

In addition to the table of Target Sizes given below, the actual sizes of the 'card' they are produced on is given by each target.

4FT TARGETS

SCORING AREAS	CIRCLE DIMENSIONS		
	TYPE 'A'	TYPE 'B'	TYPE 'C'
	500M	300M	200M
BULL	15"	9"	6"
INNER	30"	18"	12"
MAGPIE	48"	30"	30"
OUTER		48"	48"

SHOOTING RECORDS

We have included Shooting Records with the Targets, as in competition shooting the type of records you have are a replica of your target and the information is compiled on the firing point by one of your team members or a coach.

There are so many different types of record it would be impossible to illustrate all of them.

The Shooting Record Sheet shown on pages at the end of the book are to give you an idea how it is set out and the information that is recorded, but you must also keep full details of the weapons fired, number etc in your Personal Record of Training, Achievements and Conduct Booklet. ("The Little Green Book") there are also pages at the end of this Pocket Book for scores.

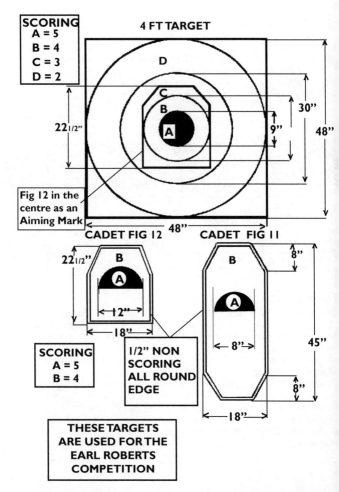

SCORING
A = 5
B = 4
C = 3
D = 2

4 FT TARGET

D

C

B

A

22 1/2"

30"

9"

48"

48"

Fig 12 in the centre as an Aiming Mark

CADET FIG 12

CADET FIG 11

22 1/2"

B

A

12"

18"

B

A

8"

18"

8"

45"

8"

SCORING
A = 5
B = 4

1/2" NON SCORING ALL ROUND EDGE

THESE TARGETS ARE USED FOR THE EARL ROBERTS COMPETITION

4-7

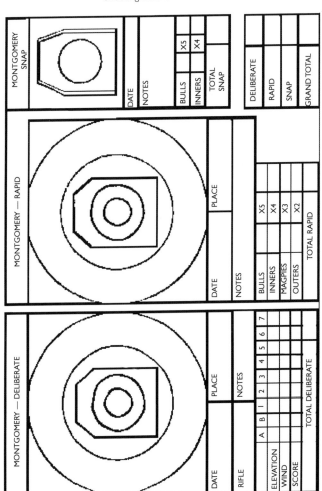

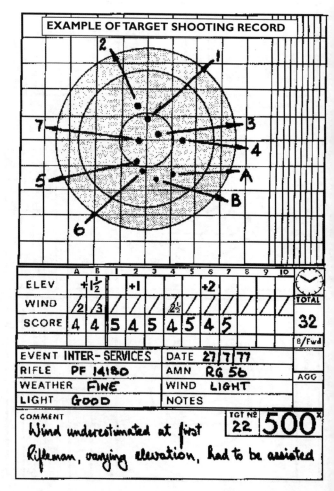

EXAMPLE OF TARGET SHOOTING RECORD

	A	B	1	2	3	4	5	6	7	8	9	10	
ELEV	+1½		+1			+2							
WIND	/2	/3	/	/	/	2½	/	/	/	/	/	/	TOTAL
SCORE	4	4	5	4	5	4	5	4	5				32

B/Fwd

EVENT	INTER-SERVICES	DATE	27/7/77	
RIFLE	PF 14180	AMN	RG 56	AGG
WEATHER	FINE	WIND	LIGHT	
LIGHT	GOOD	NOTES		

COMMENT

TGT Nº 22   500ˣ

Wind underestimated at first

Rifleman, varying elevation, had to be assisted

4-9

Chapter 5

FIRST AID

INTRODUCTION

First Aid is the immediate help given to someone who is ill or injured. Think for a moment, if you were ill or injured wouldn't you want someone to stop help and you? First aid skills are easy to learn and with regular practice and knowledge it can be of benefit through out your whole life.

First aid is not an exact science, often casualties will not respond in the way you hope. The outcomes of a casualty are not always successful, so don't be afraid to talk things through with someone if you have been affected by giving first aid treatment.

As a junior cadet, you have access to gaining the nationally recognised Youth First Aid qualification which is valid for three years, this is approved by HQ Air Cadets, a special centre of St John Ambulance. A senior cadet aged over 14 can undertake the adult first aid qualification Activity First Aid, progressing from aged 16 years to the Health & Safety Executive recognised First Aid at Work certificate.

ASSESSING THE SITUATION (AMEGR)

As a first aider when you come across a situation you must act quickly, but calmly to

Assess the situation. After finding out what happened you must remove any hazards or dangers to

Make the Area Safe, ensure you do not become a casualty. Then approach the casualty to see if they are conscious and decide to give the appropriate

Emergency Aid treatment. Once you have got the facts,

Get Help, lastly

Report what has happened to your squadron staff, they may be able to help you. You may need to clear up the squadron area, stock up your first aid kit, then brew up after all your hard work and efforts!

ASSESSING THE SCENE/SITUATION

When approaching any casualty your first priority should always be your own safety. Failure to observe this rule could easily lead to you becoming a casualty.

If you identify a hazard to either yourself or the casualty you may be able to safely remove the hazard or alternatively remove the casualty from the hazard allowing assessment to be continued in a safer location.

Every situation and scene is different but you may wish to consider the following hazards:

- Electricity
- Water
- Vehicles
- Falling objects
- Sharps e.g. Glass, knives, needles
- Aggression from a frightened casualty or bystander
- Animals
- Chemicals, if you suspect any chemicals DO NOT APPROACH. Offer advice to the casualty from a safe distance and await specialist help.

PRIMARY SURVEY

After establishing the scene is safe, the first step in every casualty assessment is the primary survey. The purpose of the primary survey is to rapidly identify immediately life threatening injuries or conditions and manage them accordingly as they are found, for example you do not check breathing before opening the airway.

The casualty should be reassessed on a regular basis using **RCEHAB.** Although this may seem excessive for the majority of casualties with minor injuries it is good practice and guarantees things won't be missed.

In a critically ill or injured casualty you might not get beyond the primary survey in the time you are with the casualty.

The sequence is as follows:
- **R**esponse
- **C**atastrophic **E**xternal **H**aemorrhage
- **A**irway
- **B**reathing

> *RESPONSE*
> *CATASTROPHIC*
> *EXTERNAL*
> *HAEMORRHAGE*
> *AIRWAY*
> *BREATHING*

Response

Is the casualty conscious?
Are they talking to you?
Ask them to open their eyes.
You may need to stimulate a response by gently shaking them by the shoulder.
This should take only a second or two.
Do not delay moving on through the primary survey if you do not get a response.

CATASTROPHIC EXTERNAL HAEMORRHAGE

Identifying and stopping a catastrophic haemorrhage is the first step in the primary survey, it is immediately life threatening if not controlled.

Recognition

Uncontrollable bleeding, often spurting or pumping
Large amount of blood lost in a short time

Causes

- Deep lacerations
- Traumatic amputations i.e. from blast injuries
- Stab wounds
- Gun shot wounds

Actions

Apply very firm pressure direct to
the site of bleeding using a clean
dressing if available.
If bleeding from a limb is
uncontrollable, apply a tourniquet
if one is available and you are
trained in its use. If you can
elevate the limb do so, this will
assist in slowing the bleeding.
In extreme circumstances
tourniquets have been improvised
using clothing and other objects but they are less likely to be effective.

Precautions
- Do not remove embedded objects
- If blood soaks through a dressing apply another dressing on top, never remove the bottom dressing as it could encourage further bleeding
- Wounds may appear small but can still bleed severely

AIRWAY

The second step in the primary survey is to open the casualty's airway.

Action
- **Head Tilt and Chin Lift Method**: Using one hand on the head and the other under the point of the chin tilt the casualty's head back, keep the airway open in this position and move on to checking breathing

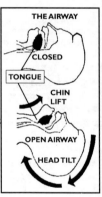

Precautions
- In incidents involving high mechanism trauma, such as road traffic collisions you may feel afraid to move the casualty and other bystanders might instruct you not to because of possible neck/back injuries. Remember, spinal injuries are very uncommon and unless the casualty's airway is opened they have no chance of survival.

Action
- **Jaw-Thrust Method:** Only used the Jaw-Thrust method when a victim who has a possible spinal injury, because it can be accomplished without extending the neck. Grasp the angles of the victim's lower jaw and lift with both hands, one on each side, displacing the jaw forward and up. Your elbows should rest on the surface where the victim is lying. If the lips close, the lower lip can be opened with your thumb. If mouth-to-mouth is necessary, close the nostrils by

placing your cheek against them. The victims head should be carefully supported without tilting it backwards or turning it from side to side. If this is unsuccessful, the head should be tilted back very slightly.

BREATHING

Look, listen and feel for normal breathing.

Action
- Look for chest movement
- Listen for breath sounds
- Feel for air on your cheek
- If the casualty is breathing normally place him in the recovery position
- If the casualty is not breathing normally, summon help and begin CPR

Look listen and feel for no more than 10 seconds. If you unsure if the casualty is breathing normally, treat as if they are not.

Precautions
- In the first few minutes of cardiac arrest (when the heart has stopped beating) the casualty may take occasional, noisy breaths or appear to be gasping. This is known as agonal breathing and is **not** normal breathing.

RECOVERY POSITION

The purpose of the recovery position is to maintain an open airway and allow drainage of blood, fluid or vomit from the mouth and nose in an unconscious, breathing casualty.

Action
- Kneeling beside the casualty, place the arm nearest to you at right angles to the casualty's body with the elbow bent and the palm facing upwards.

- Bring the other arm across the body
  and hold the back of the casualty's hand
  against the cheek closest to you.

- With your other hand lift the casualty's
  far leg above the knee so his foot is flat
  on the floor.
- Roll the casualty towards you so the
  casualty is on their side, tilt the head back
  to ensure the airway remains open.

Precautions
- If you find getting the casualty into the recovery position difficult,
  remember that the objective is to get the casualty onto their side and
  maintain an open airway. This is possible by just rolling the casualty
  towards you and holding them in position, remember the casualty cannot
  be left alone this way.

BASIC LIFE SUPPORT
If during your primary survey you identify the casualty as unresponsive
and not breathing normally they should be treated for cardiac arrest. This
is known as basic life support, or more commonly, **C**ardio **P**ulmonary
Resuscitation (CPR).

Adult basic life support sequence
Basic life support consists of the following sequence of actions:

1. Make sure the victim, any bystanders, and you are safe.

2. Check the victim for a response.
- Gently shake his shoulders and ask loudly, 'Are you all right?'

3A. If he responds:
- Leave him in the position in which you find him provided there is no
  further danger.
- Try to find out what is wrong with him and get help if needed.
- Reassess him regularly.

3B. If he does not respond:
- Shout for help.
- Turn the victim onto his back and then open the airway using head tilt and chin lift:
- Place your hand on his forehead and gently tilt his head back.
- With your fingertips under the point of the victim's chin, lift the chin to open the airway.
- If spinal injury is suspected use Jaw-Thrust method, if necessary (see page 3-4).

4. Keeping the airway open, look, listen, and feel for normal breathing.
- Look for chest movement.
- Listen at the victim's mouth for breath sounds.
- Feel for air on your cheek.

In the first few minutes after cardiac arrest, a victim may be barely breathing, or taking infrequent, noisy, gasps. This is often termed agonal breathing and must not be confused with normal breathing.

Look, listen, and feel for no more than 10 seconds to determine if the victim is breathing normally. If you have any doubt whether breathing is normal, act as if it is not normal.

5A. If he is breathing normally:
- Turn him into the recovery position.
- Summon help from the ambulance service by mobile phone, or by any means possible. If this is not possible, send a bystander for help. Leave the victim only if no other way of obtaining help is possible.
- Continue to assess that breathing remains normal. If there is any doubt about the presence of normal breathing, start CPR (5B).

5B. If he is not breathing normally:
- Ask someone to call for an ambulance and bring an AED if available. If you are on your own, use your mobile phone to call for an ambulance. Leave the victim only when no other option exists for getting help.

START CHEST COMPRESSION AS FOLLOWS:

- Kneel by the side of the victim.
- Place the heel of one hand in the centre of the victim's chest (which is the lower half of the victim's sternum (breastbone)).
- Place the heel of your other hand on top of the first hand.
- Interlock the fingers of your hands and ensure that pressure is not applied over the victim's ribs. Do not apply any pressure over the upper abdomen or the bottom end of the sternum.
- Position yourself vertically above the victim's chest and, with your arms straight, press down on the sternum 5 - 6 cm.
- After each compression, release all the pressure on the chest without losing contact between your hands and the sternum. Repeat at a rate of 100 - 120 min-1.
- Compression and release should take an equal amount of time.

Another easy method for finding the correct spot is to find the bottom of the sternum and go two finger widths up, place palm of your other hand next to these fingers then interlock the fingers. The amount that you press on someones chest varies with there size, a rule of thumb is its acceptable to compress up to one third of the body depth.

6A. Combine chest compression with rescue breaths:

- After 30 compressions open the airway again using head tilt and chin lift.
- Pinch the soft part of the victim's nose closed, using the index finger and thumb of your hand on his forehead.
- Allow his mouth to open, but maintain chin lift.
- Take a normal breath and place your lips around his mouth, making sure that you have a good seal.
- Blow steadily into his mouth whilst watching for his chest to rise; take about one second to make his chest rise as in normal breathing; this is an effective rescue breath.
- Maintaining head tilt and chin lift, take your mouth away from the victim and watch for his chest to fall as air comes out.
- Take another normal breath and blow into the victim's mouth once more to give a total of two effective rescue breaths. The two breaths should not take more than 5 seconds. Then return your hands without

delay to the correct position on the sternum and give a further 30 chest compressions.
- Continue with chest compressions and rescue breaths in a ratio of 30:2.
- Stop to recheck the victim only if he starts to show signs of life e.g. breaths normally, regaining consciousness, such as coughing, opening his eyes, speaking, or moving purposefully, otherwise do not interrupt resuscitation.

If the initial rescue breath of each sequence does not make the chest rise as in normal breathing, then, before your next attempt:
- Check the victim's mouth and remove any visible obstruction.
- Recheck that there is adequate head tilt and chin lift.
- Do not attempt more than two breaths each time before returning to chest compressions.

> *If there is more than one rescuer present, another should take over CPR about every 1-2 min to prevent fatigue. Ensure the minimum of delay during the changeover of rescuers, and do not interrupt chest compressions.*

6B. Compression-only CPR
- If you are not trained to, or are unwilling to give rescue breaths, give chest compressions only.
- If chest compressions only are given, these should be continuous at a rate of 100 - 120 min-1.
- Stop to recheck the victim only if he starts to show signs of life e.g. breaths normally, regaining consciousness, coughing, opening his eyes, speaking, or moving purposefully; otherwise do not interrupt resuscitation.

7. Continue resuscitation until:
- Qualified help arrives and takes over,
- The victim starts to show signs of life e.g. breaths normally, regaining consciousness, signs of life such as coughing, opening his eyes, speaking, or moving purposefully, OR
- You become exhausted.

SECONDARY SURVEY

The secondary survey, sometimes known as head-to-toe survey is undertaken after the primary survey, when immediately life threatening conditions have been either ruled out or identified and treated.

The purpose of the secondary survey is to establish what other injuries or presenting medical problems the casualty may have.

Action

- In a conscious casualty, ask them what has happened, or what the problem is. This will help focus your examination.
- Ask the casualty if they have any pain, noting location, description (stabbing, crushing etc) duration and any relieving or exacerbating factors, for example "it hurts when I breathe in".
- Starting at the head working down the shoulders, over the collar bones, down both arms, chest, abdomen and both legs, look and feel for signs of injury such as bleeding, bruising, swelling, deformity, reduced movement and pain.
- Ask the casualty about any current medical problems, note any medications they are on and note any allergies.
- If trained to do so, treat injuries that you find with the aim of reducing pain and slowing or stopping deterioration of the casualty's condition.

Precautions

Treat any neck or back pain following trauma, such as a fall from height or road traffic collision with caution. You should suspect serious injury if the fall is greater than 10 foot. Do not attempt to further assess a potential spinal injury and do not move the casualty unless needed for a life saving intervention, such as opening their airway.

Treat any pelvic pain following trauma with caution. Never push, rock or compress a suspected pelvic injury, do not move the casualty unless needed for a life saving intervention.

Be aware of hidden injuries. Small but devastating penetrating injuries are not uncommon in areas such as the groin, armpits and back which can be easily missed.

In a conscious casualty, always gain their permission to examine them and communicate what you are doing.

TRAUMA

The term trauma often refers to a serious injury commonly caused in incidents involving a high mechanism, such as a road traffic collision or explosion.

This section will concentrate on three types of traumatic injury.

BLAST INJURY

A blast injury is a complex type of traumatic injury. Injuries can vary greatly depending on a large number of factors, such as the cause of the blast, the proximity of the casualty to the blast and the environment in which it occurs i.e. open or confined space.

Injuries may be mostly internal and may affect predominantly hollow organs such as lungs, bowels etc. The casualty may present initially quite well **NEVER** underestimate the rapid nature at which this casualty could deteriorate.

Causes

- Explosion

INJURY CLASSIFICATION

Primary

- Injuries are caused by the blast overpressure or shock wave
- Most commonly affect the ears and hollow organs such as lungs and stomach
- Most likely to affect a casualty that is close to the explosion
- Casualty may lack external injuries

Secondary

- Injuries are caused by shrapnel and other objects propelled by the explosion
- Can cause penetrating trauma which is externally visible
- Small external wounds may conceal large internal damage and bleeding from high velocity fragments
- Secondary injuries account for a high number of blast casualties
- Improvised explosive devices may be designed to increase the number of secondary casualties by the use of nails, ball bearings or other objects surrounding the device.

Tertiary
- Injuries are caused by casualty's being thrown against solid objects such as walls or vehicles by the displacement of air from the explosion.
- Can create a wide range of injuries from bone fractures to penetrating injuries and occasionally impalements depending on where the casualty is thrown
- Smaller, lighter adults and children are at higher risk of tertiary injury.

QUATERNARY OR MISCELLANEOUS
- Any injury not included in the first three classifications
- Burns and crush injuries are examples of quaternary injuries.

> **R**esponse
> **C**atastrophic
> **E**xternal
> **H**aemorrhage
> **A**irway
> **B**reathing

Action
- Haemorrhage control and airway management (Primary Survey) Rapid transfer\evacuation to specialist care.

Precautions
- Always consider you own safety first. Could there be a secondary explosion?
- Do not underestimate a casualty's injuries, they may be internal.

BLUNT TRAUMA
Blunt trauma is a general term used when an injury is caused by an impact that does not penetrate the body. It is sometimes referred to as non-penetrating trauma.

Causes
- Physical assault e.g. punched, kicked or hit with a blunt weapon such as a bat
- Behind armour blunt trauma (injury caused by the energy transfer associated with body armour stopping a high velocity round)
- Sports injuries
- Road Traffic collision.

Recognition

- Suspect blunt trauma in any high mechanism injury i.e. where there has been high energy transfer
- Bruising, swelling and tenderness can all be signs of blunt truama

Action

- If spinal or pelvic injury is suspected keep patient still until specialist help arrives
- Internal injuries caused by blunt trauma require immediate specialist care
- Suspected chest, abdomen and pelvic injuries are time critical injuries. Do not delay getting specialist help.

PENETRATING TRAUMA

Penetrating trauma is caused by objects that enter or pass through the body (also known as perforating trauma). For a soldier, this injury type is usually associated with gun shot wounds or fragmentation injuries from improvised explosive devices. Other examples may include stab wounds and impalements.

Recognition

Penetrating trauma will usually, but not always be accompanied by pain and external blood loss

Injuries may be identified on either the primary or secondary survey

All penetrating injuries will have an entry wound

Action

- Control external haemorrhage and manage the airway as in the primary survey
- Closely monitor the casualty for signs of deterioration such as decreasing level of consciousness or increased difficulty in breathing
- In penetrating chest injury, position the casualty so the unaffected side is uppermost (injury down)
- Call for specialist help or arrange transport/evacuation without delay

Precautions

- Never remove an embedded object, it may cause further bleeding
- A small entry wound does not necessarily mean a small injury
- Look for an exit wound but there may not be one
- Remember to look in hidden areas such as armpits

SHOCK

Shock is a term commonly used by lay people to describe a state of emotional distress following an accident or injury. In medical terms it refers to a state when blood pressure falls to a dangerously low level leading to organ dysfunction and reduced levels of consciousness. Shock is hypo-perfusion of tissues, hypo-perfusion means reduced blood flow and therefore reduced oxygen. This is due to some sort of disruption in circulation, such as bleeding.

Causes

There are several causes of clinical shock. The most likely cause to be seen by a soldier is hypovoleamic shock. This is simply a low volume of blood likely to be caused by a traumatic injury. Hypovoleamic shock is the only type included in this guide however the treatment for all shock is generally the same.

Recognition

Pale, grey and clammy appearance
Increased rate of breathing
Weak, rapid pulse
Reduced level of consciousness

Actions

- Lay the patient down ensuring their airway is maintained
- Raise the patients legs
- Continually monitor the patient for signs of deterioration, be prepared to start CPR if the patient becomes unresponsive and stops breathing normally.

Precautions

- Bleeding may be internal and not immediately obvious

BURNS

Burns can vary greatly in severity from small, superficial burns to full thickness burns covering large areas of the body. The first aid treatment follows the same principle for any type of burn.

Causes
- Direct heat, e.g. flame
- Electrical
- Chemical
- Steam/hot gases
- Scald

Recognition
- Pain
- Redness (superficial)
- Red and white with blisters (Partial thickness)
- Charred or white and leathery (Full thickness)

Actions
- Stop the burning process
- Cool the burn with cool or luke warm water (not ice cold) for 10-30 minutes
- Wash off chemicals with copious amounts of water
- Once cooled, cover the burn with a non adherent dressing. Strips of cling film are ideal

Precautions
- Monitor the casualty for signs of shock and hypothermia
- Do not attempt to remove clothing stuck or embedded in the wound
- Keep the wound as clean as possible to reduce chance of infection
- Do not remove any loose clothing and other items, that may be on or attached to the injury.

HYPOTHERMIA

Hypothermia occurs when core body temperature drops below 35°C. This is the temperature required for normal function of the body's metabolism and organs.

Causes
- Exposure to a cold environment
- Immersion in water
- Wet Clothing
- Major Trauma

Recognition
- Shivering (Mild)
- Pale appearance, shaking, reduced coordination, stumbling and confusion (Moderate)
- Difficulty speaking, unusual behaviour such as removing clothing, stumbling or falling and cessation of shivering (Severe)

Actions
- Remove the casualty from the cold environment if possible
- Remove wet clothes and replace with warm, dry clothes or blankets
- In moderate to severe hypothermia, more aggressive active re-warming may be required. This can be achieved by placing warm items such as warm water bottles in the arm pits and groin areas of the casualty

Precautions
- A casualty suffering from moderate to severe hypothermia may become aggressive when confused
- Alcohol consumption increases the likelihood of hypothermia
- Complex problems can arise during re-warming of a severely hypothermic casualty, they require specialist medical treatment without delay.

HYPERTHERMIA

Hyperthermia describes a condition where the body's core temperature rises above a normal level due to an inability to dissipate heat quicker than it is absorbed. Between 37°C and 40°C can be classified as heat exhaustion. When core temperature rises above 40°C this is called heat stroke. Untreated, heat exhaustion can rapidly progress to heat stroke. When temperatures inside the body reach these levels it can cause break down of cells and organ failure. Heat stroke can be life threatening.

Causes

- Prolonged exposure to a hot or humid environment
- Extreme physical exertion
- More likely if dehydrated or alcohol is consumed
- Some medication (rarely)

Recognition
Heat Exhaustion

- Feeling sick
- Feeling Faint
- Sweating heavily

Heat Stroke

- Confusion and disorientation
- Rapid breathing
- Reduced level of consciousness

Actions

- Stop any physical activity
- If possible remove casualty to cooler area or shade
- Remove excess clothing
- Cool by fanning the casualty
- If they are conscious give them cool, not cold water to drink
- Submersing both arms up to the elbows in cool water for 5-10 minutes can quickly reduce body temperature.

Precautions

- If the actions above are followed quickly, heat exhaustion often resolves with no lasting effects after 30-60 minutes. Heat stroke however is a medical emergency and specialist help should be obtained whilst attempting to cool the casualty.

FRACTURES

Fractures or broken bones occur as a result of a direct impact or stress on the bone. In first aid they can be classified into to two distinct types, closed (simple) and open (compound)

A closed or simple fracture is when the skin is left intact. An open or compound fracture is when the skin is broken exposing underlying tissues surrounding the fracture. This is often caused by sharp ends or fragments of bone breaking through the skin at the point of injury. Open Fractures are much more prone to complications such as infection. A third category is complicated fracture when the sharp bone ends interfere and damage surrounding blood vessels and nerves.

Causes
- Direct force or impact
- High stress applied to the bone

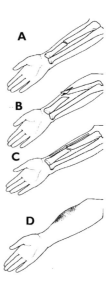

A. Closed Fracture. Skin not broken.

B. Open Fracture. Bone has broken surface of skin. Dangerous; external loss of blood and serious risk of infection.

C. Complicated Fracture. When internal nerve or organ is also injured and when fracture is connected with a dislocated joint.

D. Symptoms and Signs.
Casualty heard it break.
Pain at site of injury.
Swelling, bruising later.
Deformity, bone grating and shock.

Recognition
- Pain
- Swelling
- Deformity
- Reduced range of movement
- Visible bone (open fractures)

Actions
- Manage and control external bleeding
- Immobilise the affected limb in a position that is comfortable, this may be as simple as providing support or padding
- Cover open wounds with a clean, preferably non-adherent dressing. If there is bone protruding from the skin, bandages can be used either side of the bone to provide padding and protection.

Precautions
- Fractures are usually very painful. Do not let them distract you from higher priority injuries. Always complete your primary survey.
- Large bones such as the femur (thigh bone) and the pelvis require very high forces to cause a fracture and can cause significant, even life threatening internal blood loss. Monitor for signs of shock and do not delay getting specialist help.
- Be aware of other complications e.g. interruption of blood supply to are below breaks.

SEIZURES

Seizures vary greatly in their appearance and are caused by a number of physiological and sometimes psychological conditions. The type of seizure most people will be familiar with or recognise is most commonly seen in epilepsy. Sudden, chaotic electrical activity in the brain causes the casualty to become rigid followed by an episode of uncontrollable convulsing or shaking. This is known as a tonic-clonic seizure. Undiagnosed epilepsy is possible in a soldier, however other causes of seizures should also be considered. All seizures need to be investigated at a hospital.

Causes
- Epilepsy
- Head injury
- Low blood pressure

- Low oxygen levels, for example following a period of airway obstruction or breathing difficulties
- Hypoglycaemia (low blood sugar)
- Recreational drugs
- Conditions affecting the brain, such as tumours

Actions
- Maintain an open airway
- Lay the casualty down if possible preferably on their side
- Move objects away from the casualty that may cause them injury whilst they are convulsing/fitting
- Loosen tight or restrictive clothing.

Precautions
- Never try and restrain someone that is having a seizure
- Seizures burn a huge amount of energy, once the casualty has stopped convulsing they may remain very drowsy or sleepy for hours - called Post Ictal Period.
- Casualty's may bite their tongue during a seizure causing a potential airway obstruction from bleeding
- Most seizures last only seconds and are self limiting, however be prepared for repeated seizures
- Do not delay in getting specialist help. A seizure may be the sign of a serious underlying condition or injury. A continual seizure is a life threatening condition. A Continual seizure is a fit where the patient does not regain consciousness once the fit has ended and another fit happens. Longer than 40 mins may cause significant brain injury.

CASUALTY POSITIONS

When you have identified what is wrong with the casualty, take the time to make them more comfortable, and assist recovery, here are a few suggestions.

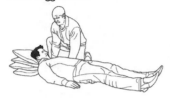

IF ITS IN THE HEAD RAISE THE HEAD, laid down with head raised, used for head injuries, unless spinal is suspected, or eye injuries.

IF THE FACE IS PALE, RAISE THE TAIL, raising the legs should calm the casualty down and slow bleeding

IF ITS IN THE CHEST SITTING IS BEST, the half sitting position, sat up, supported knees raised, useful for chest injuries, conscious heart attack casualties, breathing problems, massive allergic reactions.

IF ITS THE ABS PROP KNEES WITH A BAG, this position with the casualty laid down and the knees slightly raised is the suggested position for fractured pelvis and abdominal wounds.

Chapter 6

MAP READING

INTRODUCTION - MAPCRAFT

Map reading is an interesting, useful skill to possess as a civilian, it can broaden your horizons and give you safe access to the countryside. Maps reach back through our nation's history and have always been important. As a cadet you need to be proficiency at map reading and navigation is an important skill. The National Navigation Awards Schemem helps to develop navigation skills, helping people to enjoy the outoors safely and with confidence. You can learn it yourself and then further your skills by getting out on the hills for the weekend or taking part in orienteering which is a fun, competitive activity.

Practice makes perfect and you'll get a real sense of accomplishment when you get it done well. A good, reliable, steady map reader is a prized asset to any squadron or flight.

With practice and dedication your map reading skills will be as sharp as your skills you learning the ACO. In addition to being able to navigate, locate your position if you get lost and tell how long a leg will take, skilled map readers can study the map and visualise the ground in their "minds-eye". This is the real prize, they will swiftly be able to make an assessment of the best route to get to there destination quickly and safely.

CARE OF MAPS

In the British Isles, maps are produced by the Ordnance Survey, military maps are produced by the RLC's Mapping Dept and can be tailored to suit a particular requirement,.

Maps should be protected, they are made of paper, and wont survive repeated soakings, place them in a map case, there are many types of waterproof map cases available.

RELIABILITY OF MAPS

A map is a 'birds eye view' of the ground, and is accurate only at the time it is drawn. Modern mapping is produced by satellite technology and aerial photography, but as time goes by the 'picture' on the ground changes, villages expand, new roads are laid, woods are cut down and others planted etc... For every day map reading purposes, this will not affect the accuracy too much, but it should be borne in mind. In a nutshell if the map you've been issued is 25 years old, it will be considerably less accurate than one printed this morning.

MARGINAL INFORMATION

Maps should include 'marginal information' this provides guidance on how to read the map and how to interpret the detail, refer to this until you have a complete understanding of what all the symbols (usually called Conventional Signs) and other information mean, but do not be tempted to cut them off to save weight/space.

The number of your map and its scale will be found at the top of the map. The index to adjoining sheets is shown as a diagram near the bottom right hand corner of the map. You will need to find out which sheet number you require to cover the particular area that you are using and the next sheet if your route goes "off the map". Most maps now use metres as the "unit of elevation", check your map by looking in the margin at the bottom of the map as "ELEVATIONS IN METRES".

THE GRID SYSTEM

The British National Grid System divides the whole country into 100 km sq squares, these squares are further subdivided by GRID LINES printed on the map. GRID LINES are the way you 'pinpoint' a specific spot on your map.

Maps are printed with the North at the top of the sheet, one set of GRID LINES run up and down the map (North and South), the others run across the map (East and West).
It is important that you are able to find a point on the map and then be able to go out and find it on the ground, also to be able - at all times - to indicate on the map the exact place where you are standing on the ground.
To assist in the accurate use of the grid system it is advisable to obtain a Pathfinder Protractor/Romer, it provides two of the different scales of GRID SQUARES found on Ordnance Survey Maps. This Romer is made of rigid plastic which you place on the GRID SQUARE of the map and read off the figures as described below, to pinpoint the exact position.

FOUR AND SIX FIGURE REFERENCES

When giving a reference there are a few simple rules to remember:-
1. FIRST - count the figures along the BOTTOM of the map, from left (west) to right (east) these are called 'EASTINGS'.
   Next count the figures up the sides of the map, from bottom (south), to top (north) these are called 'NORTHINGS'.
2. A reference must always contain an even number of figures
3. GRID REFERENCES are always given with the 'EASTINGS' value first, followed by the 'NORTHINGS' value.

The example in the diagram opposite, shows a black square, that can be given the reference as square 8040 (a four figure reference). This square could represent a whole square kilometre of ground, not exactly a 'pinpoint' location on a map or ground.

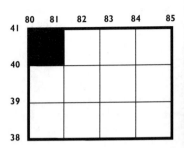

Should you use a four figure reference, you must add a feature to indicate where you mean. To get an exact position, the square is further subdivided into 10 squares in both directions.

The diagram (centre below) illustrates this subdivision, the black square is **"square 7 - 7**, these figures when added as explained below make up a six figure reference

The first two figures the **EASTING** value, followed by the sub divided square figure, then the two **NORTHING** value figures, followed again by the sub divided figure, making up a six figure reference **807407**.

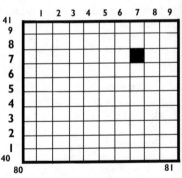

ALWAYS ORIENTATE YOUR MAP FIRST

SETTING A MAP WITH (SILVA) TYPE COMPASS

The first essential drill on the ground with a map is to 'set it' or sometimes know as 'orientating' your map.

Until you do this it is difficult to establish your exact position on the map/ground. Carry out the following:

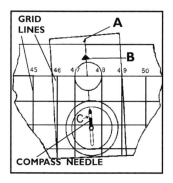

1. Lay your map out flat, find the **MAGNETIC NORTH ARROW**
   - usually in the margin of the map as shown at 'A' on the diagram opposite.
2. Lay the base of your Silva Compass on the map with the D**IRECTION TRAVEL ARROW (B)** in line with the **MAGNETIC NORTH** (see diagram 'line-up')
3. Carefully turn the map and compass round - watching the compass needle swinging, until the **RED MAGNETIC END** of the **COMPASS NEEDLE (C)** coincides with the **DIRECTION OF TRAVEL ARROW (B)** and the **MAGNETIC NORTH ARROW (A)** on the map.

Your map is now set or orientated, in relation to the ground.

SETTING A MAP WITHOUT A COMPASS BY OBSERVATION

This can be easy, once you have identified exactly where you are on the map, and if you are standing on a straight road, line up the road on your map with the road you are standing on.

Make certain that the map is pointing in the right direction, i.e. the right way round.

If not on a road, you will need to find other objects on the ground such as a road/track junction, church, prominent hill top or farm buildings.
You must also find and identify the same objects on your map, using them as shown in the diagram below by turning your map to set or orientate it in relation to the ground.
North, East, South and West are known as the cardinal points of the compass.

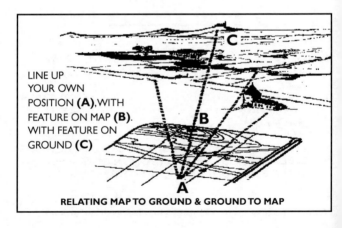

LINE UP
YOUR OWN
POSITION **(A)**, WITH
FEATURE ON MAP **(B)**
WITH FEATURE ON
GROUND **(C)**

RELATING MAP TO GROUND & GROUND TO MAP

THE LIGHT WEIGHT (SILVA TYPE) COMPASS

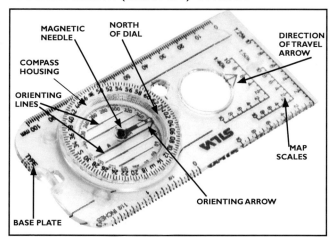

CARDINAL POINTS OF THE COMPASS

There are 32 points of the compass, but only 16 of them are normally used in map reading for the description of direction. These 16 are the four cardinal points and 12 intermediate points as shown in the diagram on the next page.

The letters **N, S, E** and **W** stand respectively for **NORTH, SOUTH, EAST** and **WEST**. In the intermediate points these letters are combined, e.g. **SE** is South East. **NNW** is North North West, etc.

These points describe direction only to within one sixteenth of the full circle: for more accurate indication of direction it is necessary to use subdivisions of the circle using "mils" or "degrees".

The mils system is used by the Military to give much greater accuracy than degrees.

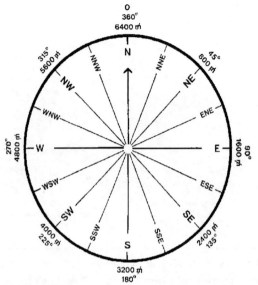

The **MILS SYSTEM** divides the circle of the compass into 6400 MILS, the zero being at the North Point.

The four quadrants or quarters of the circle are each 1600 mils, and so the East, South, and West points fall at 1600, 3200, 4800 mils respectively, as illustrated.

The symbol normally used to represent mils is the character letter m, with a / across it, and appears as ɱ.

NORTH POINTS

There are **THREE** NORTH points:

1. **TRUE NORTH** - The actual direction of the geographical North Pole..
2. **GRID NORTH** - The direction of the vertical GRID LINES on a map. For all practical purposes TRUE and GRID NORTH are the same.

3. MAGNETIC NORTH -

The direction towards which the compass needle is attracted is the MAGNETIC NORTH POLE, **(MN)** see the diagram on the right.

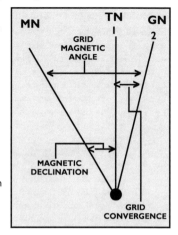

ANGLES BETWEEN NORTH POINTS

Grid Magnetic Angle. (GMA)

This is sometimes called the magnetic variation and is the angle between GRID NORTH and MAGNETIC NORTH it depends on two factors:

1. **TIME.** As the position of the Magnetic North Pole moves slightly eastwards, so the GMA (Grid Magnetic Angle) changes. This is called the Annual Magnetic Change and must be taken into account when converting magnetic bearings to Grid Bearings and vice versa.

2. **PLACE.** The GMA (Grid Magnetic Angle) also varies from one part of the country to another. These two factors are included in the marginal information on the map.

MAGNETIC DECLINATION

This is the angle between MAGNETIC and TRUE NORTH as shown on the diagram.

GRID CONVERGENCE

This is the angle between GRID NORTH and TRUE NORTH which can, in practice, be ignored since for practical map reading purposes TRUE NORTH and GRID NORTH are the same.

BEARINGS - TYPES OF BEARINGS

As there are three types of North points, there are three kinds of bearings, according to the North point from which they have been measured:

1. **A MAGNETIC BEARING** is one taken with a compass (an accurate compass needle always points towards MAGNETIC NORTH).

2. **A GRID BEARING** is one measured on a map with the Silva compass used as a protractor or using your Pathfinder Protractor/Romer.

3. **A TRUE BEARING** cannot be measured direct, but must be calculated from the other two. However this can be ignored for practical map reading purposes.

> **NOTE. INDIVIDUAL COMPASS ERROR (ICE)**
>
> *The accuracy of each individual compass is subject to error, it is important that you should check your own compass to establish the **INDIVIDUAL COMPASS ERROR (ICE)**, do this by checking it against other compasses. Having done so make a note of it on your compass base with a small sticky label, don't forget to allow for it.*

TO TAKE A MAGNETIC BEARING

1. Point the compass direction of march arrow at the object.

2. Turn compass housing until the red arrow is under the needle.

3. Read off the MAGNETIC BEARING on the compass housing
   One of the most common uses of taking bearings is to take one from the map to find the bearing to march on with your SILVA type light weight compass or your protractor which is quite simple.

TO TAKE A GRID BEARING

NOTE: IGNORE THE COMPASS NEEDLE.

a. Place the long edge of the compass along the desired line of travel, making sure that the DIRECTION OF TRAVEL ARROW **(1)** on the compass POINTS IN THE DIRECTION of your LINE OF TRAVEL **(2)**

b. Turn the COMPASS NEEDLE HOUSING **(3)**, so that NORTH on the housing rim points to NORTH on the map.

You will notice that the ORIENTING LINES **(4)** on the COMPASS are parallel to the GRID LINES **(5)** on the map - or they should be.

c. Read the number of mils/degrees against the DIRECTION OF TRAVEL LINE at **(6)**, this is the GRID BEARING. Having taken a GRID BEARING from the map, you must take into account and make allowances for the GRID MAGNETIC ANGLE (GMA)

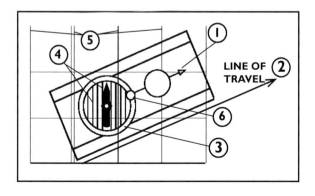

FINDING YOUR
POSITION WITH A COMPASS - RESECTION

There may be times when you need to find your exact position both on
the map and on the ground. This could be as a result of being "dropped-off"
on an exercise or if you were unfortunate enough to crash land in wild
country. You could find your position by using a compass and following the
instructions set out below.

You will need to refer to the diagram on this page.

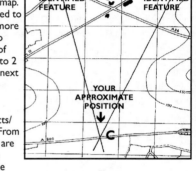

1. Set/orientate your map. Select
   TWO prominent objects or
   features which you can be
   sure of identifying on the map.
   These objects/features need to
   be a good distance away, more
   than 1000 metres and also
   be separated by an angle of
   approximately 10 o'clock to 2
   o'clock - see diagram on next
   page.

2. On the "plastic" cover of
   your map, mark the objects/
   feature at **"A"** and **"B"**. From
   the position at which you are
   standing, (call it **"C"**) take
   a bearing on to each of the
   objects/features in turn, writing down the bearings. As this has to be
   accurate, don't move from your position and take a further two bearings
   on both of the objects/features. Add together the three bearings to each
   object/feature and divide by three to get the average bearing to each.

3. These are COMPASS Bearings, they are MAGNETIC Bearings.
   As you are to use them to 'plot on a map', they have to be converted
   from MAGNETIC to GRID Bearings.
   NOTE: You will always be best advised to draw a small diagram - until

you become familiar with working with bearings - showing the NORTH POINTS as shown on page 8-8, this will remind you to make an allowance for the GMA (Grid Magnetic Angle).

The current GMA is approximately 50 mils (3^0) This is the figure that you would subtract from the MAGNETIC BEARING.

REMEMBER: "MAG TO GRID - GET RID"

4. Check the resulting bearing and adjust it to the nearest 25 mils. Remember the settings or divisions on the compass card of a Silva or Light Weight Compass are 25 mils.

5. Now set up the GRID BEARING on your compass for bearing **"A"**. Use a wax pencil with a fine point , put the point on **"A"** . Hold it in a vertical position, place the long edge of the compass against the pencil with the DIRECTION OF TRAVEL ARROW pointing in the direction of **"A"**, and the NORTH ARROW pointing approximately to the top of the map.

6. Using the pencil still in a vertical position, pivot the compass about the pencil point until the NORTH ARROW points exactly towards the top of the map, with the edge of the compass or any of the red setting lines on the compass base parallel to the nearest GRID LINES on the map.

7. Hold the compass firmly in this position while you draw a line along the side of the compass.

Repeat the same procedure from point **"B"**.

Where the two lines you have drawn from **"A"** and **"B"** cross each other is your calculated position on the map/ground. Now work out your exact six figure GRID reference of your location.

CONVERTING A GRID BEARING TO A MAGNETIC BEARING

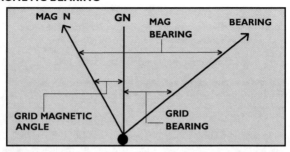

Remember all bearings are measured in a clockwise direction from the **NORTH** point. A **MAG** bearing will always be **GREATER than the GRID** bearing taken, by the amount of the **GRID MAGNETIC ANGLE**. Therefore to convert **GRID to MAG ADD** the **GRID MAGNETIC ANGLE (GMA)**
To convert a **MAG** bearing to a **GRID, SUBTRACT** the **GRID MAGNETIC ANGLE.**

GRID MAGNETIC ANGLE

(GMA) in UK is as follows:
GMA = $2.^0 55"$ or 33.5 mils West in July 2012* (*approx.)
*GMA changes yearly and you can get an accurate GMA reading from:
http://www.geomag.bgs.ac.uk/ data_service/models_compass/ gma_calc.html

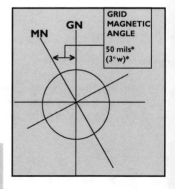

> **REMEMBER**
> **"Grid to Mag - ADD"**
> **"Mag to Grid get RID"**

IDENTIFYING A FEATURE

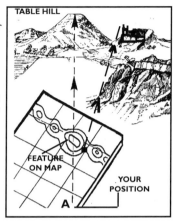

Set your map, use the edge of your protractor or a pencil, place it on the map with the edge running through your position, swing it across the map until it lines up with the feature on the ground. The feature should be easy to pick out, provided it is not too far away and that it is on your map!

This like so many Map Reading skills need constant practice until you carry it out as a "drill" and second nature.

After a while you will be able to locate and identify features by just looking across the map.

In setting your map, no matter what method you use, it is the constant relating and comparison of the map and ground which will build a good foundation for your navigational skills.

We remind you that this skill above all will go a long way to prevent you getting lost.

Practice, Practice Practice, then mapreading will be a natural skill

MARCHING ON
A BEARING

Having converted your GRID BEARING to a MAGNETIC BEARING, set the graduated circle to read the MAGNETIC BEARING at the DIRECTION OF TRAVEL line.

Then turn the whole compass until the NORTH end of the NEEDLE coincides with the NORTH ARROW and is parallel to the MERIDIAN LINES on the COMPASS HOUSING, holding the compass in front of you, march in the direction indicated by the LINE OF TRAVEL ARROW. So long as the compass needle and the NORTH ARROW are kept together, the DIRECTION OF TRAVEL ARROW will remain on the required bearing.

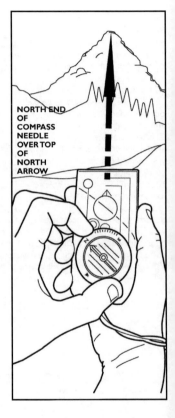

NORTH END
OF
COMPASS
NEEDLE
OVER TOP
OF
NORTH
ARROW

BACK BEARINGS WITH A SILVA COMPASS

When marching on a bearing - especially at night - over some distance you may often have a

doubt in your mind that you may go wandering off course and finish up being lost. The ability to use your compass and to trust it by taking a back bearing on to the point from which you started, will prevent you getting into difficulties. The simplicity of the Silva compass makes the use of back bearings an easy navigational aid.

To use the compass for a BACK BEARING, keep the compass on the bearing you have taken (as 'X' to 'Y' in the diagram), rotate the COMPASS HOUSING through 3200 mils(180°). The compass is now set to march on the **BACK BEARING** (in the direction of 'Y' in the diagram) of your original **FORWARD BEARING.**

To retrace your route - (from 'Y' to 'X' march on the bearing given as your **BACK BEARING.**

This is a very important skill - easily learned with a compass, it is one of the best methods of preventing yourself from getting lost.

"Practice makes perfect"

FORWARDS AND BACK BEARING

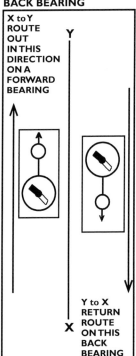

X to Y
ROUTE
OUT
IN THIS
DIRECTION
ON A
FORWARD
BEARING

Y

Y to X
RETURN
ROUTE
ON THIS
BACK
BEARING

X

HILLS AND VALLEYS

The method of showing how the ground is shaped in terms of the hills and valleys which are expressed as the **RELIEF,** are shown by **CONTOUR LINES.** These appear as thin brown lines on the map and are described as "an imaginary line joining all points of equal height above sea level". You must check the information at the bottom of the map near the scale diagram to find the "Contour Interval", that is the height between each contour.

To give you a better understanding of contours the following pages of information and diagrams will explain them.

UNDERSTANDING AND INTERPRETING CONTOURS

Contours are quite easy to follow, provided you understand the fact that they follow the same height, round hills, into re-entrants, and over the spurs.

They do not provide a picture of the shape of the land, but with practice and using contours you will be able to interpret the shape of the ground from the contour lines - mapcraft at its best!

Until you have mastered your map craft it is difficult to know from a contour whether the ground is rising or falling, whether the feature is a spur or a re-entrant.

A spur projects out from the land mass, while a re-entrant is exactly the opposite - a shallow valley running up into the mass.
It is not always possible, however, to tell which is the top of the slope and which is the bottom, without being able to find the contour figures.

When the contour figures can be read with both the map and the figures the correct way up you would be able to tell if the ground is rising or falling.

A general idea of which way the slopes run can be obtained by looking at other features - particularly lakes, ponds, rivers, streams, and railway lines.

A stream running near a set of contours indicates at once which is the bottom of the slope.

Similar features such as railways, villages and large woods are more likely to be found at the bottom of a hill than at the top.

CONVEX AND CONCAVE SLOPES

A CONVEX slope is one that bulges outwards, and a **CONCAVE** slope is one that curves inwards - see the diagrams on the right.

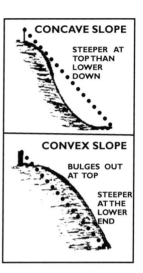

CONCAVE SLOPE

STEEPER AT TOP THAN LOWER DOWN

CONVEX SLOPE

BULGES OUT AT TOP

STEEPER AT THE LOWER END

Standing at the top of a **CONVEX** slope you would not be able to see all the way down to the bottom, because the outward slope would obscure your view. This is important to recognise as ground that you cannot see - "dead ground" it can conceal the enemy or give you cover from view.

When standing at the top of the **CONCAVE** slope, however, there would be a clear view the whole way down the slope.
It is important to be able to recognise these two types of slopes from the map.

CONTOUR VALUES

If you had several paths right round a hill, each one keeping at the same level, and were walking round one of them, you would find that where the paths were near to each other the ground would be steep between them, and where the paths were some distance apart, the ground would slope gently, the further they were apart, the less the slope would be.

SPOT HEIGHTS AND TRIG POINTS

Apart from contours, height is shown by **SPOT HEIGHTS** which is marked on a map by a dot and number ●241. This is the exact height in metres or feet above sea level.

You will also find **TRIG POINTS**, shown on the map as a small black triangle with a number next to it ▲576 this again is the exact height above sea level. This Conventional Sign will go out of use in future years as advanced methods of map making come into use.

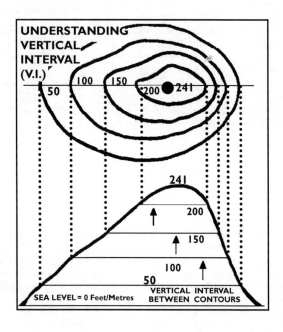

MORE ABOUT CONTOURS

On gentle slopes the **CONTOURS** are far apart, on steep slopes the **CONTOURS** are close together.

You do not need to find the figures on the contour lines to give you a 'picture' of the ground in an area, the contour lines show quite simply the comparative steepness of the slopes, the SPURS and **RE-ENTRANTS**.

If the ground is broken and rugged there will be many SPURS and **RE-ENTRANTS** and your path will be constantly turning in and out.

Broken, rugged country is shown by irregular, sharply turning contours.

Where the slopes are smooth, your path will curve gently, bending out as it follows the line of a SPUR and swinging in at a **RE-ENTRANT**.

On gentle slopes the contours appear as smooth flowing curves.

The contours may appear to wander about all over, but if you follow them they naturally come back to where they started from, the only exception to this is when you find a cliff face with a sheer drop, then all the contour lines are so close together they appear to be one.

Every curve or bend in a contour indicates a SPUR or a valley, a rise or fall in the ground, just as it does on the side of a hill. Remember - the distance the contours are apart still indicates the steepness or flatness of the ground.

Heights of Contours - see illustration on previous page - Understanding Vertical Interval (V.I.)

Each contour is drawn at a specific height above sea level and each one is the same vertical height above the one below. The difference in height between contours is called the Vertical Interval (VI).

These heights are written into the contour lines at intervals along their length.

On Ordnance Survey maps the figures showing the height of the contours are always written so as they read facing up hill, it is important to remember this as you can very quickly find out which direction the ground is sloping.

Check the information in the margins of the map to find out if the **VI (Vertical Interval)** is in Feet or Metres.

Whenever you are "out on the ground', you should look at the ground formation in the area, draw those imaginary contour lines around the hills and valleys, make a rough sketch and then get a map of the area and see how well you have been able to interpret the ground.

CONTOURS AND THE SHAPE OF GROUND

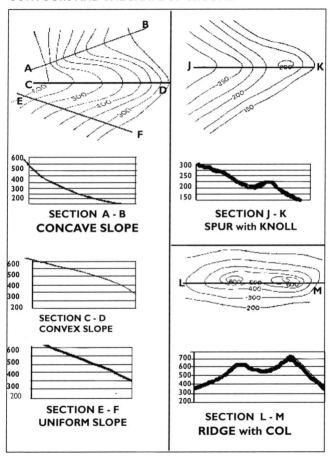

SECTION A - B
CONCAVE SLOPE

SECTION J - K
SPUR with KNOLL

SECTION C - D
CONVEX SLOPE

SECTION E - F
UNIFORM SLOPE

SECTION L - M
RIDGE with COL

KNOW YOUR CONTOUR PATTERNS

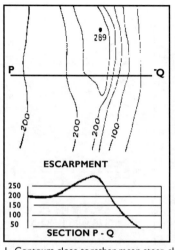

ESCARPMENT

SECTION P - Q

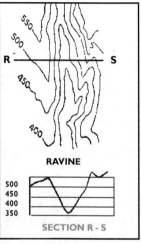

RAVINE

SECTION R - S

1. Contours close together mean steep slopes.
2. Contours far apart mean gentle slopes.
3. When contours are evenly spaced the slope is uniform, these slopes have small undulations and pockets of dead ground.
4. When the spacing of the contours reading from high ground to low, decreases, the slope is convex. Convex slopes mean short visibility; dead ground becomes very close.
5. When spacing of contours, reading from high to low, increases, the slope is concave.
   Concave slopes mean good visibility and little dead ground.
6. Wandering contours at various distances apart and never close, mean undulating ground. Important to note the general direction of the fall in the ground.
7. Gently curving contours indicate an area of country of rounded slopes. As the ground becomes steeper the contours come closer together, as it becomes more rugged the curves disappear and the contours take on 'jagged' shapes.

SCALES AND MEASURING DISTANCE

The scale of a map is the relationship between the actual distance measured from one point to another on the ground and the distance between the same two points on a map.

The way that the 'scale' of a map is expressed is by the Representative Fraction. It used to be expressed in words, e.g., "one inch to one mile", or "four miles to one inch".

This is now being superseded by the **RF** method.

The Representative Fraction (RF) is the standard method used on all continental maps and wherever the metric system is used.

Most British maps are now expressed in metric. It is simple to use if you remember that the RF is 1/X, one unit of distance on the map represents X units of distance on the ground.

For example, a scale of 1/50,000 means that one inch/centimetre/metre on the map represents 50,000 inches/centimetres/metres on the ground.

The essential connection is that the SAME unit of measurement applies both to the map and to the ground measurement.

A distance of 2cms on a 1/50,000 map therefore represents 2 x 50,000 cms on the ground = 100,000 cms = 1000 metres.
All maps are printed with graphic linear scales, usually in the centre of the bottom margin, from which any horizontal distance may be measured on the map in kilometres and metres, or in miles and yards.

A linear map scale is always shown in the form of a diagram as Next page.

Referring to the diagram below, you will notice that the zero mark is set from the left of the scale by one major division, which is then subdivided into ten (or other suitable) subdivisions usually not longer than about 4 mm each. Measurements falling between any of these subdivisions must be estimated.

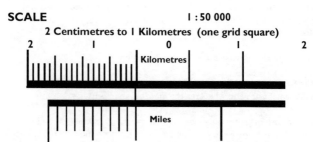

SCALE   **1 : 50 000**

2 Centimetres to 1 Kilometres (one grid square)

1 Kilometre = 0.6214 mile   1 Mile = 1.6093 Kilometres

NOTE: The above diagram is NOT to scale, but to illustrate the scale found on a 1: 50 000 map.

LINEAR MAP SCALE.

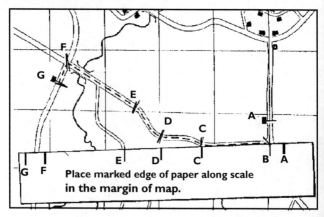

Place marked edge of paper along scale in the margin of map.

HOW TO MEASURE DISTANCE

Make a mark on the straight edge of a piece of paper, put the mark on the point you wish to measure from and make successive marks along the edge of the paper as you follow the route from your starting point to the final point.

This is easy if you just want to measure along a straight road, but if it means going round corners you will have to pivot the paper and make several marks as you progress.

The total distance is then recorded along the edge of the paper.
Lay the paper along the scale on the map, with the right hand tick against one of the major divisions, so that the left hand tick lies against the subdivision to the left of the zero mark. The total distance is then the number of major divisions plus the distance to the left of the zero.

With practice this is quite an accurate method of measuring distances.

NAVIGATING ROUND OBSTACLES

Obstacles are often found on a route and in order to keep a really accurate direction you should make a diversion by going round them. This is done by plotting a series of right angles and measuring by paces as illustrated in the diagram below 200 paces, 500 paces, 200 paces, bringing you back on the original bearing.

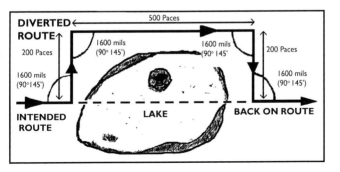

FINDING TRUE NORTH FROM THE SUN USING A WATCH

When you do not have a map or are map reading without a compass, it can help if you are able to find the rough direction of TRUE NORTH or SOUTH.

The method explained below will give you an approximate direction - not accurate enough for reading bearings or other measurements.

INFORMATION - as the sun rises in the EAST, and moves (in the northern hemisphere) through the southern sky, setting in the WEST, the position of the Sun, when visible, is always a rough guide to the direction of NORTH.

A watch when set to Greenwich Mean Time (GMT) for UK (or to local time for other areas some distance EAST or WEST of Greenwich) may be used. If summertime or other artificial time is in local use your watch should be adjusted to Greenwich Mean Time (GMT) or to the local standard time.

METHOD - lay your watch flat, with the HOUR HAND pointing to the sun.

In the NORTHERN hemisphere, TRUE SOUTH will then be midway between the hour hand and twelve o'clock on the watch - see diagram above. In the SOUTHERN hemisphere, lay your watch with twelve o'clock pointing to the sun. TRUE NORTH then lies midway between the hour hand and twelve o'clock. When the sun is high up in the sky, this method cannot be used with any success. In any case the result is unlikely to be accurate to better than five degrees.

NIGHT MARCH

Before a night march, the bearings should be worked out and the compass set by day. As much of the route should be reconnoitred by day - even from a distance. Ground studied from Aerial Photographs if available. Landmarks, roads, hedges, streams etc that have to be crossed should be noted as a check on distance and direction.

Several compasses may be used with bearings preset for each 'leg'.
If visibility allows pick out an object on the required bearing, as far distance as can be clearly seen, and march to it. Then select another object, march on that and so on.

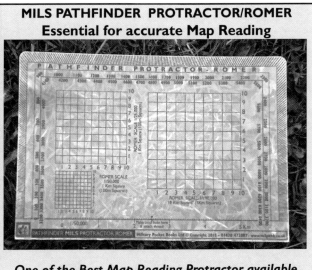

MILS PATHFINDER PROTRACTOR/ROMER
Essential for accurate Map Reading

One of the Best Map Reading Protractor available
direct from www.milpkbk.co.uk

FINDING TRUE NORTH

By the stars

(Northern Hemisphere)

In latitudes less than 60⁰ the **POLE STAR** is never more than about 40 miles away from **TRUE NORTH**. The position of the **POLE STAR** is indicated by the "pointers" of the Great Bear or Plough - see diagram. All stars revolve round the POLE STAR and the Plough may be either below it low down near the horizon and "right way up", or above it in the sky and "upside down" or in any position between.

If the Plough is obscured or below the horizon, **Cassiopeia** which is shaped like a **W** and is on the opposite side of the POLE STAR from the Plough, may be visible; the POLE STAR is the nearest bright star within the arms of the **W**. Above 60⁰ latitude the POLE STAR is too high in the sky to be a good guide to NORTH.

At the NORTH POLE it is vertically overhead.

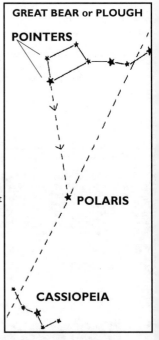

The only way to learn night navigation is to get out in the dark, identify the constellations shown in the above diagram and practice moving in different directions by using stars and checking with your compass.

ROUTE CARDS

The purposes of a ROUTE CARD is to ensure that you plan the route you are taking and from the start become aware of the distances you are proposing to travel and the obstacles that you will encounter. Planning how to overcome them or taking action to find a route round them, Plan RV's points and the locations for your bivi sites, importantly to ensure that in an emergency, assuming you have had the sense to leave a copy - someone will know your approximate position at any given time.

The illustration of the ROUTE CARD below is self explanatory, you need plenty of space in each column to write information. Never be short of detail, it is better to have more than you need than not enough.

If you are in a group make sure each person has an accurate copy and leave a copy behind for someone who you will be in contact with during your expedition or exercise.

The importance of CHECK POINTS and the TIMES that you are to be there must be shown on the ROUTE CARD.

ROUTE CARD

Date_____

Produced by_____ Start Point Grid Ref_____ ETD ___

Date Finished .... Finishing Point Grid Ref .... ETA ....

| Leg | From | | To | | Bearing | | Distances | Remarks |
	Location	Grid Ref	Location	Grid Ref	Grid	Mag		Landmarks Hazards
	EXAMPLE OF HEADINGS AND LAYOUT FOR MAKING ROUTE CARDS							

TERMS USED IN MAP READING

BEARING: The angle, measured clockwise, that a line makes with a fixed zero line. It may be a True Bearing, measured from True North - a Magnetic Bearing measured with a compass from Magnetic North, or a Grid Bearing measured from Grid North.

COL (SADDLE): See also SADDLE for description.

CONTOUR: An imaginary line on the surface of the ground at the same height above mean sea level throughout its length. Contour lines are drawn a map to show the shape of the ground.

CREST: The highest part of a hill or range of hills. That line on a range of hills or mountains from which the ground slopes down in opposite directions.

DATUM or DATUM LEVEL: The level from which altitudes are measured; generally mean sea-level.

DETAIL: All the topographical information on a map.

DIVIDE: The line along a range of hills from which the water flows in opposite directions, e.g., the continental divide.

ESCARPMENT: The steep hillside formed by a drop in land level, usually at the edge of a plateau.

FIXED POINT: Used in making a map to denote a point that has been fixed on the paper by survey methods.

GORGE: A narrow stream passage between steep rocky hills; a ravine with precipitous sides.

GRADIENT: A slope described by a percentage, mostly used on roads to indicate the rise and fall in a road; e.g., a steep hill.

GRATICULE: Lines of longitude and latitude drawn on a map as the basis for a system of map references.

GRID: Lines drawn on the map forming squares as a basis for a system of map references.

GRID NORTH: Except through the origin, grid lines do not lie true north and south or east and west. Grid North is the direction of the north-south grid lines on a map.

HACHURES: A conventional method of showing hill features by shading in short lines drawn in the direction of the slope. thicker at the top of the slope than at the bottom.

HORIZONTAL EQUIVALENT (HE): The horizontal distance on the ground between two adjacent contours.

ISOGONAL: A line drawn on a map through places having the same magnetic variation.

KNOLL: A small knoblike hill.

LEFT or RIGHT BANK: The appropriate bank of a stream or river when facing DOWN stream.

LOCAL MAGNETIC ATTRACTION: Attraction of the compass needle due to presence of metal or magnetic iron ore. NOT to be confused with Magnetic Variation.

LUBBER LINE: Sometimes referred to as the HAIR LINE running through the glass lid of the Prismatic Compass, used for sighting on an object when taking a bearing.

MAGNETIC VARIATION or DECLINATION: The angle between True North and Magnetic North.

MAGNETIC NORTH: The point in far north of Canada, to which a compass needle points.

MERIDIAN: A true north and south line.

ORIENTING a MAP: Placing it so that its True North line points True North (or Magnetic or Grid North line points to Magnetic or Grid North). This is also called "Setting the Map".

PLATEAU: A table land: A raised plain, usually quite flat, above a level of the land.

PLOTTING: Transferring to a map bearings and other measurements.

RAY: A line drawn from the position of an observer to fix the direction of an object.

RAVINE: A long deep valley worn by a stream

RE-ENTRANT: A shallow valley or ravine, usually between two spurs, running inwards towards the hill or mountain top. Usually found where a stream runs off a hillside.

RIDGE: The line along a hill or range of hills or mountains from which water flows in opposite directions; a divide; sometimes the crest of a line of hills as it appears along the horizon.

RESECTION: The process of finding a position by taking bearings on two identifiable points and plotting them on a map, also by fixing a position by observation of at least two previously identified points.

SADDLE: A depression between adjacent hill or mountain tops: also called a col.

SECTION: A line drawn to represent the shape of the surface of the ground along a line between two points.

SPOT HEIGHT: A point on a map whose height has been found by survey methods, identified by a dot with figure against it.

SLOPES: (Concave and Convex): Convex "bulges out", Concave "caves in".

SPUR: A hill feature or low ridge, running out from a hill or high ground, often found between two re-entrants.

TRIG POINT: A concrete pillar with a brass mounting used by Ordnance Survey for their survey work. The correct name is a Triangulation Point. Marked on a map by a small triangle with the height above sea level shown next to it.

TRUE NORTH: The direction of the North pole from that point.

VERTICAL INTERVAL (V.I.): The difference in level between two adjacent contours on a map.

WATERSHED: The line, usually mountain range where waters divide to flow into different river systems; the edge of a river basin.

GLOBAL POSITIONING SYSTEMS (GPS)

Global Positioning System is a small, battery powered, hand held receiver, that helps you locate yourself on the ground, by picking up signals from satellites in stationary orbit around the earth. Each model, and there are lots of them, has different features so we can't teach you how to use it, but they come with easy to understand instructions, so instead here are a few tips. GPS is a "War winning bit of kit" a senior officer was heard to say during the First Gulf War. The ability to give you an accurate grid reference wherever you are in the world has obvious advantages when you're out and about. However nothing is 100% reliable and you should bear in mind a few things when using it. The batteries run down, and do so quickly with constant use, depending on the model you're using, so make sure you've got a fresh set of batts on you when you start and take some spares. Try to ensure they're the same type as other battery powered things you're carrying, this will save weight as you won't have to double up. Get it out and use it, it's an incredible bit of kit, but you need to dedicate a few hours to really finding out what it can do, have a play with it. The displays can crack with rough treatment so take care of it, if it's on your pocket you can wrap it in your gloves or woolly hat. GPS relies on a clear view of the sky to give you a triangulated position, so make sure you are not standing next to a large building, in a basement, or at the bottom of a cliff, in a street with not much view of the sky, because if the unit can't see at least three satellites you won't get a really pinpoint position. Bear this in mind when you are in woods, forest or in the jungle, you will have problems, as the unit might not able to see the sky (Remember those 6 P's)

Prior, **P**reparation, **P**revents, **P**retty, **P**oor, **P**erformance.

Reliance on GPS may mean that you neglect your map reading, so if the unit goes down, you might be up to your neck in it, use GPS as a check nav and for confirmation, but always keep on top of your map reading with compass and map, or at the very least, ensure you have the correct mapping and know where you are so you can sort yourself out with your map. Always reboot/turn on your GPS before you set off, so that it can get its bearings, especially if you have travelled across borders, the unit might be confused and crash.

Don't wait till you need it urgently to switch it on and find that it's not working.

As with anything in life,
rely on it but not too much!

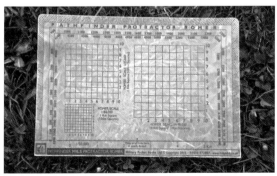

One of the Best Map Reading Protractor available
direct from www.milpkbk.co.uk

Chapter 7

FIELDCRAFT

INTRODUCTION

The principal skill to be successful at escape and evasion is to be expert at applying Fieldcraft in any given situation. It is a subject most enjoyed as it is usually fun and gets you and your `mates' to turn out in strength, especially if it says on the programme that it's going to be an *Escape and Evasion* exercise, if it's at night - so much the better.

We are not suggesting that all cadets still like playing `cowboys and Indians', but perhaps Fieldcraft could be described as organised cowboys and Indians!.

If you live in a city/town you are at some disadvantage to see Fieldcraft in action, however, if you are able to get into the countryside or live in or near it, you will be aware that the wild life `get a living' off the land by being experts in the use of their skills of; stealth, patience, speed and fitness, stamina, planning and cunning and being natural experts at camouflage and concealment.

NATURAL SKILLS

Fieldcraft is their prime skill in catching their food and in many ways to be good at Fieldcraft you could do no better than to study wildlife at every opportunity.

Observe how a cat stalks its quarry, how the Sparrow Hawk, hovers patiently, observing the right moment to drop in on the Field Mouse, how the Fox who uses the hedgerows to move from one field to another, see how well a Rabbit is camouflage against the ground, all of these examples are types of Individual Fieldcraft skills exercised for the purpose of either *defence or attack*.

In your case, having knowledge of Fieldcraft brings together and practices some of the skills required to evade capture or to act effectively as a sentry.

INDIVIDUAL SKILLS

Once you have an understanding of the need to imitate those skills that wild life practice to survive in the field, then you will be on the way to attaining an acceptable standard of Individual Fieldcraft.

Even when you are mentally and physically fit, you will need a lot of practice and patience, to develop the natural ability to react in defence of your

survival, both as an individual and as a member of a group.
Be good at fieldcraft and survive - you seldom get a second chance.

METHOD OF JUDGING DISTANCE

WHY JUDGE DISTANCE; if you can judge distance you will know the
approximate area in which to look when given an order. If your sights are not
correctly adjusted on the range, your shots will probably miss the target.

USE A UNIT OF MEASURE

100 metres is a good unit, The Range is marked out at 100 metre intervals.
A Full Size Football pitch is about 100 metres long.

**DO NOT USE THE UNIT OF
MEASURE METHOD OVER
400 METRES IF YOU CAN'T
SEE ALL THE GROUND
BETWEEN YOU AND THE
TARGET AREA/LOCATION**

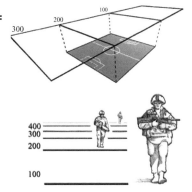

USE COMMON OBJECTS FOR APPEARANCE METHOD

AIDS TO JUDGING DISTANCE

When you know what 100 metres looks like, practice fitting your Unit of Measure between you and a target.

APPEARANCE METHOD

By noting what a person looks like at a set distance, you can then use the Appearance Method. Common objects may also be used for this method.

THINGS SEEM CLOSER

FURTHER AWAY

REMEMBER

Things seem closer .. In bright light, if they are bigger than their surroundings, if there is dead ground between you and them, if they are higher up than you.

Further away ... With sun in your eyes, in bad light. When smaller than surroundings. Looking across a valley, down a street or along a path in a wood, if you are lying down.

KEY RANGES

If the range to one object is known, estimate the distance from it to the target.

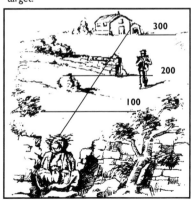

BRACKETING

Calculate mid-distance between nearest possible and furthest possible distance of target.

Nearest   - 100
Farthest   - 300
Mid-distance - 200

HALVING

Estimate the distance halfway to the target then double it:
100 x 2 = 200

PERSONAL CAMOUFLAGE AND CONCEALMENT

**The enemy is looking for you so - don't make it easy.
Merge with your surroundings**

TOO MUCH   **JUST RIGHT**   **TOO LITTLE**

LOSE YOUR SHAPE

Make sure nothing shines.
Blend in with your
surroundings - if
they vary, so
must you

**AVOID
SKYLINES**

Stand back from
merge into the shadows -
don't lean out
You **WILL BE SEEN**

SOMETHING IS SEEN BECAUSE OF ITS:-

Shape
Shadow   } IS FAMILIAR OR STANDS OUT
Silhouette

Surface   } IS DIFFERENT FROM ITS
Spacing   } SURROUNDINGS
Movement

SEEING IS ... ... NOTICING DETAILS

EASY TO SEE   **DIFFICULT TO FIND**

SHAPE .... Disguise you shape - including equipment
and weapons.

SHADOW .... Keep in the shadows

SILHOUETTE .... Don't skyline

SURFACE .... Don't differ from your surroundings.

**SPACING ...... ** Keep spread out - but not equally spaced.

**MOVEMENT ...... ** Move carefully - slowly when concealed - sudden movement will attract attention.

Look through cover - if possible - not round it.
You **MUST SEE** without being **SEEN**.

TARGET RECOGNITION
The correct target must be located and fired at

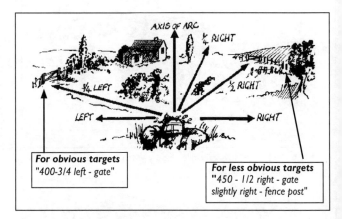

For obvious targets
"400-3/4 left - gate"

For less obvious targets
"450 - 1/2 right - gate
slightly right - fence post"

For difficult targets use the Clock Ray Method -

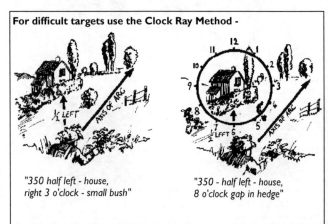

"350 half left - house,
right 3 o'clock - small bush"

"350 - half left - house,
8 o'clock gap in hedge"

MOVE QUIETLY AT ALL TIMES

Keep your weapons out of the mud.

MOVEMENT AT NIGHT

Movements used during daylight are not suitable at night-they have to be adapted.

THE GHOST WALK

Lift legs high, sweeping them slowly outwards. Feel gently with toes for safe place for each foot, put weight down gently.; Keep knees bent. Use the left hand to feel the air in front of you from head height down to the ground checking for obstructions, trip wires, booby traps or alarms etc.

THE CAT WALK

Crawl on hands and knees. Search ground ahead for twigs, move knee to where hand has searched.

THE KITTEN CRAWL

It is quiet- but slow. It is very tiring. Lie on your front, search ahead for twigs, move them to one side. Lift your body on your forearms and toes, press forward and lower yourself on to the ground.

NIGHT NOISES

At night you hear more than you see.
Stop and listen.
Keep close to the ground,
turn your head slowly and use a cupped
hand behind the ear. Freeze if you hear
a noise.

MOVING AT NIGHT - REMEMBER

Keep quiet .... have no loose equipment. Move carefully ... use the Ghost walk, Cat walk or Kitten crawl.

Clear your route by hand, search carefully in front of you ... dry vegetation will make a noise.

Use available cover ... flares, thermal imaging and night observation devices will turn night into day.

Keep to the low ground ... you split your party at night at your peril.

LISTENING AT NIGHT

If the enemy is about - keep an ear close to the ground. The closer you are to the ground, the more chance you have of seeing the enemy on 'skyline'. Keep your mouth open this opens your ear canal and aids your hearing.

NIGHT VISION

We can see in the dark - but REMEMBER our eyes take 30 minutes to get used to the dark.
We see less than in daylight. We see shapes - not detail.
We see skylines and silhouettes. We may see movement.

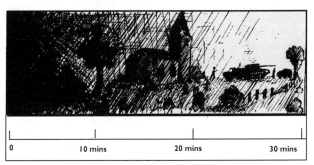

| 0 | 10 mins | 20 mins | 30 mins |

YOUR EYESIGHT

Your eyes have two sets of cells, one set for daylight (CONES) in the centre of your eyes, the other set for darkness (RODS), which are around the CONES.

The night cells work when the day cells are affected by falling darkness. With constant practice night observation can be improved. If you have a cold, headache or are tired it can reduce your night vision.
You will find that there is a limit to the time you can concentrate effectively on any given point or your vision becomes blurred.

Most service units use Thermal Imaging (night sights) that "turn darkness into daylight" in as much that they pick out an object giving out heat (body heat).

The SUSAT sights on the SA80 MK2 Rifle (an optical sight) has advantages similar to that of binoculars for night observation.

BRIGHT LIGHT RUINS YOUR NIGHT VISION

If caught in the light of flares take cover at once in open ground. If in a wood - FREEZE. If you see a flare, quickly close one eye to protect your night vision, use the other eye to look about you taking advantage of the light, but do not move suddenly as this will give you away.

DUTIES OF A SENTRY

Sentries are the eyes and ears of the squadron. If they do their job well, their squadron will be safe and secure.

When you are a Sentry make sure:-
That you know and understand your orders. That you know what to do if your post is approached by a person or vehicle.
That you ask questions if you do not understand anything.
What ground to watch. Direction of the enemy.
Signal for defensive fire.
Names of prominent landmarks.
Where neighbouring posts are situated.
Information about patrols that maybe in the area, or coming through your post.

SENTRIES AT NIGHT IN THE FIELD

At night sentries work in pairs.

Sentries must know:-

1. What to do if anyone approaches their post.
2. What ground to watch.
3. The Password.
4. Sentries close to the enemy must know :-

   Direction of the enemy.

   Name of land marks.

   Where neighbouring posts are.

   Signal for defensive fire.

   About patrols that may come in or out through their post or near them.

HOW TO CHALLENGE.

When you see movements which you think
may not be your own forces - alert your
Patrol Commander.
Say **'HALT' HANDS UP.**
'Advance one and be recognised'. 'Halt'.
Give the challenge half of the password -
quietly, so that only the first man can hear it.

ACTION - Allow friendly forces through,
know how many and count them through -
one at a time.
Section opens fire at enemy troops.

NOTE

Be aware of a common trick which is for the enemy to approach a sentry,
listen and learn the first half of a PASS WORD then fade away.
An inexperienced sentry may allow this to happen. The same enemy then
approaches another sentry and challenges them before they can challenge
them.

Again the inexperienced sentry might then give the reply then allow the
enemy into their position.
So be careful and never allow anyone into your position unless you can
positively identify them, when in doubt call for help.

USE YOUR SENSES.

What are your senses, how can they help in Fieldcraft? On a patrol or on
duty as a sentry you will use your EYES and EARS, and your TOUCH
when feeling your way through woods or difficult cover.
Your sense of TASTE may not be used, but your sense of SMELL —
depending upon the SMELL — may remind you of taste. SMELL can give you
away and the enemy. Body smell or the smell of cooking, or anything else
drifts on the air and can give away your position.

CHOOSING A ROUTE.

If you have to advance across country, check that you know where to make for. Then decide on the best route.

REMEMBER

Routes must be planned ahead.
You must move in bounds or stages from one observation point to another.
You must check your direction - are you keeping on course.

ALWAYS USE A COMPASS

Must not be seen but should be able to observe without restriction.
If you have to take a risk choose a route which offers the risks early in your approach rather than later on, since you will have less chance of being seen.
The best route will - have places to observe the area - without being seen yourself.
Don't go blindly on towards and into an unknown area.
Give good positions and cover for sentries.
You must be able to take offensive action if necessary.
Let you move without being seen.
Not to have impassable obstacles such as marsh land or open ground or ravines.

PACING

Pacing is necessary because you must always know how exactly far you have gone when counting a number of your own 'paces'.

You should know your 'Pacing Scale', over different types of ground conditions, I.E. Tarmac roads or tracks, grassland, woodlands etc.

To find your PACING SCALE, put two markers out 100m apart. Walk the distance between them as you would on a patrol, counting the paces as you go.

If it has taken you 120 paces to cover the 100m, then that is your PACING SCALE.

It follows, to use this scale if you were on a patrol and had to go a distance of 300m, you would have to count out 360 paces.

Under some conditions you can use a specific length of string, tying knots at every 120 paces. Having used the length of string, un-tie the knots and repeat the process on the next 'leg' of your route.

It is always advisable to have a CHECK PACER, remembering to check that your PACING SCALE is the same by day and night.

NAVIGATION

This is the art of moving from one place to another and consists of three important stages that MUST be carried out if you are to be successful, they are as follows:-

1. **PLANNING**
2. **KEEPING DIRECTION**
3. **GOOD PACING**

PLANNING -You must plan your route in advance, using maps, air photos, sketches and information from previous patrols or recces.

KEEPING DIRECTION - Always take several compasses and as many 'pacers'. Always get someone else to check your navigation, at both the planning stage and while you are executing the movement.

It is often hard to keep direction, especially at night, in fog or in close country.

When it is necessary to make a detour to avoid an obstacle or seek cover, it is easy for leaders to miss the correct lines of advance.

AIDS TO KEEPING DIRECTION.

Some of the aids to keeping direction are:-

a. The compass, map and air photographs.

b. A rough sketch copied from a map or air photograph.

c. Keeping two prominent objects in view.

d. Using a series of easily recognisable landmarks, each visible from the previous one.

e. The stars and also the sun and moon if their natural movement in the sky is understood.

f. Memorizing the route from a map or air photograph. Helpful details are the direction of streams, distances between recognisable features coupled with pacing, and the course of contours.

g. Trees in exposed country tend to grow away from the direction of the prevailing wind. Moss may grow on the leeward side of tree trunks.

h. Remembering the back view, patrols and others who may have to find their way back should look behind them from time to time and pick up landmarks to remember for the return journey.

j. Leaving directions marks on the outward journey, these may be pegs, small heaps of stones.

k. If the route is being walked by day by those who are to guide along it by night, they must take note of skylines and objects or features which they will be able to recognize in the dark.

SELECTING OF LINES OF ADVANCE.

Remember the keyword - **'G R O U N D'**

G	Ground from the map. The type of ground; Open/close country, Rolling/flat.
R	Ridges, water courses and watersheds (highest) mark on map or talc.
O	Observation – good view points.
U	Undergrowth - study woods, scrub, trees, villages.
N	Non Passable obstacles, such as rivers, ravines, marsh land.
D	Defilade covered lines of advance and areas which offer cover can now be selected.

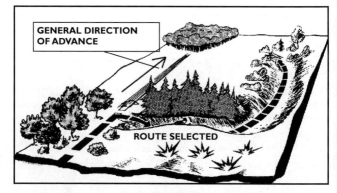

OBSERVATION — SEARCHING GROUND

The skill of searching ground is based upon learning to `scan' an area using an accepted system.

It will test your concentration and exercise your knowledge of `why things are seen' and the principles of Camouflage and Concealment.

In the diagram we have - for the purpose of illustrating to you — drawn lines across the landscape.

In practice you would choose prominent features, landmarks, roads etc., and draw your imaginary lines across the landscape through these reference points.

SCANNING

As seen in the illustration on the previous page, the landscape is divided into **FOREGROUND, MIDDLE DISTANCE** and **DISTANCE**. You can further divide this by indicating a centre line (again based on reference points), calling left of the line **"LEFT OF ARC"**, and right of the line **"RIGHT OF ARC"** as shown in the illustration.

Having divided the landscape, the correct method is to scan each area horizontally (left to right or right to left).

View the area in short overlapping movements in a very precise manner, especially any features that are at an angle from your position.

SEARCHING

While scanning you may see something move or that requires further investigation. There may be an area where you may come under observation from, it would be as well to check that out early.

Weather conditions can give you a clue when searching, frost on bushes, foot marks will show up clearly, if the weather is hot camouflaged positions can be given away when leaves or grass dry off changing colour.

Search across hedges and rows of trees , NOT along them. At all times consider WHY THINGS ARE SEEN.

PYROTECHNICS — BLANK AMMUNITION & THUNDER FLASHES, FLARES AND SMOKE.

As an Air Cadet you *may be involved* in exercises with the RAF Regiment or other Cadet Forces (including the CCF) where Blank Ammunition, Thunder Flashes, Flares and Smoke generators are used.

You **must be made aware** of the Safety Standards required when taking part in training where pyrotechnics are to be used.

All pyrotechnics by their very nature contain explosive materials.

Without exception they are all very dangerous, especially if used in a confined space or explode within a few feet of you.

Loss of sight and hearing, badly burned hands and faces are serious injuries sustained by individuals from pyrotechnics.

You will be told when pyrotechnics are in use and instructed as to the correct Safety Precautions to be observed by all ranks taking part in the exercise.

NO CADETS WILL BE PERSONALLY INVOLVED IN THE OPERATION OF THUNDER FLASHES, SMOKE GENERATORS OF ANY TYPE OR FLARES OF ANY DESCRIPTION.

SELF TEST QUESTIONS

1. To be good at Fieldcraft you need to have what.
2. For what reason do you use: Unit of Measure. Key Ranges. Bracketing.
3. Give an example of "Unit of Measure".
4. When carrying out Personal Cam what do you have to remember.
5. What is "Isolated cover", would you use it.
6. Why are things seen, what must you remember about "smell".
7. What is important about Shape, Shadow, Silhouette.
8. Silence when moving at night, how do you prevent any noise from your kit you are wearing/carrying.
9. Explain the use of 'the clock ray method'.
10. Give a method of moving at night.
11. How long does it take for your eyes to get used to the dark.
12. When a FLARE "goes up", what do you do.
13. When do sentries work in pairs.
14. What are the Duties of a Sentry.
15. What is the correct CHALLENGE a sentry should give, when and how should it be given.
16. What helps you to listen at night.
17. A Sentry close to the enemy must know — What.
18. Give the three important points to consider when "choosing a route".
19. How do you work out your own PACING SCALE.
20. Give six methods used to help you Keep your Direction.
21. How do you split up an area you are going to SCAN and SEARCH.
22. In daylight, you must not fire a blank at anyone less than, how many metres away, and at night what is the rule.
23. What is the Key Word "GROUND" used for, and what does it indicate.

SAFETY WARNING FIRING BLANK AMMUNITION
With all field training when blank ammunition is in use,
NEVER aim directly at any cadets or adults,
**DO NOT AIM AT ALL IF THEY ARE LESS
THAN 50 METRES AWAY FROM YOU.**

Chapter 8

FLYING

The likelihood is being an Air Cadet you already have some interest in flying. The opportunities open to you within the ATC are dependent on your efforts on squadron, and your attempts to reach the required standards of training. You must qualify as a First Class Cadet to be considered for any flight training (or as a minimum, pass your Airmanship, Navigation and Communications modules).

Flying with the ATC is free, so take advantage of it. There is no other organisation that gives you an opportunity like this! It is also a chance to put into practice some of the skills and knowledge you have learnt at your squadron.

Before you can get airborne, there is one very important document that you have to have signed and completed; that is the Parent or Guardian's Consent to Fly form. This forms part of your 3822A, held at your squadron.

In the following paragraphs we will set out some of the opportunities to fly within the Corps, from your first AEF through to a Flying Scholarship.

AIR EXPERIENCE FLYING

Opportunities for cadets to fly were provided from 1958 to encourage an interest in aviation. These flights are available at many different locations within the RAF. Air Experience Flights (AEF) are commanded by RAF pilots, assisted by staff pilots who are members of the RAF and RAF Volunteer Reserve, with previous experience as full time pilots.

They fly the Grob 115e, known in the RAF as the Tutor T1. It is a two-seat, single-engine aircraft with dual controls. Usually, the pilot sits in the left seat and you will sit in the right seat. The aircraft is fully aerobatic, so as well as learning standard manoeuvres, you may be invited to experience some aerobatic flight.

The Tutor has side-by-side seating with dual controls, which enables you to take control of the aircraft when asked, so as to put into practice what you have learnt.

You can expect to fly at least once a year with the local AEF, as well as on annual camps to other RAF stations.

Before you fly, try to think about what you would like to learn from each flight, as the pilot will probably ask if you have any specific requests.

FLIGHT SAFETY

Before you are allowed to fly in the Tutor, you will be given a full safety brief. This includes what to do in an emergency. You will get the brief every time you attend the AEF, and you must pay attention. The brief may have changed from your last visit, and you won't remember everything anyway. The brief will tell you the following information:

a. Donning of your parachute and LSJ (Life Saving Jacket) if needed
b. How to enter the aircraft, and where it is safe to tread
c. Where to sit in the aircraft, with assistance from ground crew
d. How to fasten your harness
e. Use of the radio communication equipment

EQUIPMENT

You will be provided with a flying suit, parachute, LSJ if flying near water, helmet, gloves, boots and a sick bag. A safety equipment fitter, or "Squipper" for short, will assist the fitting of your parachute, and adjust your helmet accordingly. Your sick bag is important - if you are sick you must tell your pilot immediately, who will fly straight and level and provide ventilation to help. If you think you will be sick, get your sick bag out immediately. If you make a mess of the aircraft, it may be rendered unserviceable for a day or two. Many people feel airsick when they fly, even very experienced pilots, so don't feel embarrassed if you do feel unwell.

ENTERING THE AIRCRAFT

You will be escorted to the aircraft, and approach from the rear of the aircraft, to enter the right hand side of it. The wings of a Tutor are glass-reinforced plastic (GRP), and therefore are very fragile. Marked in black are the areas where it is safe to tread on.

Your escort will also help you get strapped into the aircraft.

The seat harness is fitted securely to the aircraft, and ensures you won't fall out of the seat if inverted. It consists of two waist straps, which should be connected first, two shoulder straps and one "g" strap which go between your legs. The harness straps all connect to one Quick Release Box, or QRB. Your headset lead will be plugged into the aircraft's communication system.

YOUR FLIGHT

When the pilot is ready he will taxi the aircraft away from the dispersal, and get permission from Air Traffic Control to take off. On average, you should get 30 minutes flying, with some hands-on experience. When the pilot is not busy talking to Air Traffic Control or other aircraft, make sure you talk to them and try to observe as much as possible in flight. On returning to the airfield, you should ensure your 3822 is updated with your flight details.

TUTOR T1: GROB 115E

The TUTOR entered RAF service in 1999 and serves the RAF's Elementary Flying Training Schools (EFTS), University Air Squadrons (UAS), and Air Experience Flights (AEF). It replaced the Scottish Aviation Bulldog T1, itself successor to the long-serving de Havilland Chipmunk. It is a side-by-side, single-engine aircraft with dual controls. It offers superb visibility and is fully aerobatic.

Technical Details:

Wingspan	10m
Length	7.4m
Crew	2
Normal Operating Speed	100kts ASL
Engine	1 Avro Lycoming
	4-cylinder piston engine

THE PARACHUTE

This is a seat type parachute with a soft rubber seat cushion on which you sit.

The two shoulder straps **(A)** are brought over the shoulders and allowed to hang vertically.

The leg straps **(B)** are brought over the thighs and passed through the leg loop **(C)** which protrudes from the parachute pack itself.

The leg straps must pass up through the loop and the metal lugs **(D)** are pushed into the bottom slots of the quick-release box **(E)** which is fitted to the large webbing strap **(F)** which comes round the left of the body.

The operating knob **(E)** of the quick-release box has three positions - fastening, locked and unlocked.

When pushing in the lugs, this knob must be turned anti-clockwise and held in the fastening position where it is spring loaded and will automatically return to the locked position when released.

When the lugs of both leg straps are correctly in place in the quick-release box, the lugs of the shoulder straps are inserted into the top slots of the quick-release box - again holding the knob in the fastening position.

The harness is now adjusted by first tightening the leg straps by pulling up on the loose ends then tightening the shoulder straps by pulling down on the loose ends.

The harness should be a good, tight fit such that you should be able to stand only in a stooped position.

To release the parachute harness after your flight, rotate the operating knob **(E)** of the quick release box to the unlocked position and PRESS.

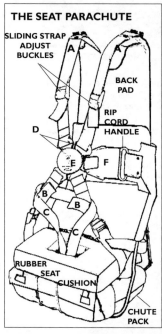

THE SEAT PARACHUTE

SLIDING STRAP ADJUST BUCKLES

A

A

BACK PAD

RIP CORD HANDLE

D

E

F

B

B

C

C

RUBBER SEAT CUSHION

CHUTE PACK

LIFE PRESERVER (OR MAE WEST)

If you are liable to fly over water, you will be supplied with a life preserver waistcoat. If you need to use it, will be inflated by a carbon monoxide cylinder when the beaded handle is pulled downwards. It will enable you to float in a safe and comfortable position in the water.

HEADSET AND MICROPHONE

You will be provided with a headset and a safety helmet. The headset plugs into the aircraft communications system by means of a jack plug. There is an on-off switch on the microphone which should be kept in the 'off' position except when you are speaking in order to minimise the level of engine noise for the pilot.

LOOSE ARTICLES

Ensure that you remove everything from your pockets before a flight since loose articles can lead to jammed controls which could be disastrous.

AIR SICKNESS

You will be provided with a sick bag in case you feel unwell at any stage during the flight. Should this occur, tell the pilot you feel unwell, he will then fly the aircraft straight and level and open the cockpit slightly to give you some fresh air. If you are sick, remember to catch it all in the sick bag otherwise if you make a mess of the aircraft no one else will be able to fly today.

In order to avoid the possibility of air sickness, you should tell the pilot if it is your first flight and he will fly accordingly. Remember, you do not have to do aerobatics unless you wish to and if these should cause you to become unwell, tell the pilot immediately.

ACTION IN AN EMERGENCY

Emergencies in the Tudor T1 are extremely rare. However accidents can happen. If an emergency arises:-

> a. Do not panic.
> b. Do as you are told.

If an emergency arises the pilot will tell you about it and give the order "Check parachutes" - do so by ensuring that the parachute straps are tightened.

The pilot will then, at the appropriate time, open the cockpit by sliding the canopy back as far as he can.

You must slide it back to its full extent by grabbing the handle marked with black and yellow stripes and sliding the canopy right back.

When the pilot decides that the aircraft must be abandoned, he will give the order "Jump, Jump" upon which you will:

a. release the aircraft safety harness (this is the blue one - do not release the parachute harness)

b. unplug your headset and microphone

c. stand up in the cockpit

d. jump head first over the side of the aircraft aiming to clear the trailing edge of the wing. It is vital that you do this immediately the pilot has ordered "Jump, Jump".

e. when clear of the aircraft, look at and pull the metal rip chord handle as far as you can - it comes out a l-o-n-g way. (the rip cord handle is known as the "D" Ring)

This releases the parachute which will allow you to float safely to the ground with an impact rather like jumping off a wall 3 - 4 metres high.

OPPORTUNITY FLIGHTS

When on summer camp or a station visit, it is very common for cadets to receive flights in multi-engine or rotary-wing aircraft with an operational or traing squadron.

THE AIR CADET PILOT SCHEME

The award has three "streams", AEF, Civil Powered and Civil Microlight.

AEF - On an AEF, flying the Tutor, you will undertake a residential course, usually a couple of weeks long. You will complete a course of around 12 hours, covering a syllabus similar to the RAF's EFT course up to solo standard (but due to safety regulations, Air Cadets cannot fly the Tutor solo).

Civil - At a selected flying school, you will learn to fly a single-engine light aircraft, and if you are competent, fly solo. These courses are usually residential.

Both of these courses when successfully completed, will gain your Flying Scholarship wings, with a "P" in the centre.

Microlight - This course offers 12 hours instruction on a microlight aircraft at a civilian school, with the chance to fly solo. On completion, you will receive microlight wings with an "M" in the centre.

THE AIR CADET PILOT NAVIGATION SCHEME (ACPNS)

This course provides you with flying and ground instruction in navigation techniques for pilots. It is only available at certain AEFs. On completion you are awarded an Air Cadet Navigator's Brevet.

CIVILIAN FLYING SCHOLARSHIPS

ROYAL AIR FORCE ASSOCIATION - The RAFA offers four

scholarships a year, one for a full NPPL and three smaller awards of 12-15 hours. The scheme is open to all cadets of the ACO aged 17 and over, subject to academic and medical requirements. The scholarships are provided as a thank you for support given in past Wings Appeal campaigns, and will go to the cadets who they feel deserve it most. Selection is usually through a short aptitude test and interview. Application forms and up to date details can be found at: **www.rafa.org.uk**

THE AIR LEAGUE EDUCATION TRUST - The ALET offers about

50 scholarships a year of about 12 hours each, with one winner deemed to have made the most progress awarded funding for a full NPPL the following year. These scholarships are advertised late in the year, to be flown the following summer. All are gifts from members of the Air League or sponsored by outside bodies. The scheme is open to Air League members over 17 and under 26. Selection includes an interview and a short aptitude test.

The ALET also offers a bursary scheme for young PPL holders, as well as one full balloon PPL scholarship.

Details can be found on their website: **www.airleague.co.uk**

HONOURABLE COMPANY OF AIR PILOTS AND AIR

NAVIGATORS - These scholarships cover all aspects of training up to licence issue for a candidate who is prepared to dedicate a considerable part of the summer to gaining their PPL. Providing up to 45 hours of flying, these scholarships can take a candidate with little or no experience to completion of their flying licence during the course of the summer, alternatively they can "finish off" someone who is already partially trained. The scholarships are awarded entirely on merit as evidenced on the completed application form and as assessed by a selection committee appointed by the Company. Candidates must be 17 or over on 1 June of the year of application and the course must be completed by the beginning of October - website: **www.gapan.org**

Battle of Britain Pilot
Wing Commander Bob Doe, DSO, DFC & Bar
in his Spitfire DAZ, shoot down 14 enemy aircraft.

Chapter 9

PRINCIPLES OF FLIGHT-GLIDING

"To every action there is an equal and opposite reaction" is one of Newton's famous laws. This is easily understood by thinking of a person swimming. The water is pushed backwards (that is the action) and your body is propelled forwards (equal and opposite reaction). Consider one further example: the wheels of a motor car revolve, the tyres push backwards on the road and the car moves forward.

So how can this simple idea explain whet happens to an aircraft in the air? To answer this question it should first be realised that air, too, is a substance like water and if you like - the road or ground. Consider what happens whenever there is a strong gale, for example, it may be difficult to walk or it may be possible to lean against the air currents. This proves that air is a real substance, even though it is invisible.

SIMPLE EXPERIMENT

On fixed wing aircraft, it is the wings that produce the LIFT (which balances the weight of an aircraft, if the lift of an aircraft is greater than the weight, then the aircraft rises - and vice versa). To demonstrate how 'lift' is produced by a wing, a simple experiment is shown.

A Hold a piece of card so that it is slightly raised at the front (similar to a real wing) Push the card forward fairly rapidly, and you will see the card rise and try to fold backwards.

This is very similar to what happens when an aircraft speeds along the runway - the wings produce enough LIFT to carry the aircraft off the runway. It is now possible to look at all the forces that act on a real wing.

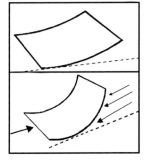

CROSS-SECTION OF WING

NOTE: THRUST is the result of the power from the engine(s)
DRAG is the resistance produced from the whole aircraft.
So far we have seen that LIFT is the key factor.

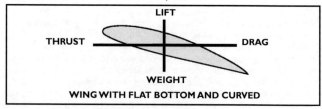

WING WITH FLAT BOTTOM AND CURVED

But how is this LIFT produced?
To explain this, consider another experiment.
Blow along a sheet of paper, lift is produced.
By blowing along the piece of paper, notice it rises. Now consider a typical aircraft wing:-

CENTER OF PRESSURE

A simpler way to imagine all these forces acting on the wing, is to sum these up and show them as a single arrow. This is obviously an easier way to show the LIFT FORCE than drawing lots of arrows. It is also normal practice to show this single arrow acting at one particular point on the wing -known as the Centre of Pressure. See the diagram on the next page.

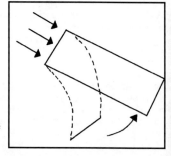

This is similar to balancing a ruler on your finger by finding the centre of gravity - i.e. the middle of the ruler.

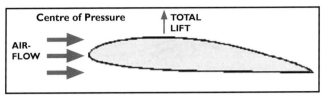

HOW LIFT VARIES

The amount of lift a wing produces depends on a number of factors:

1. The airspeeds of an aircraft.
2. The angle of attack.
3. The air density.
4. The shape of the wing cross section.
5. The total wing area.

Naturally, if the speed of an aircraft is increased (as it speeds along the runway) the more and more LIFT is produced. The angle of attack of an aircraft (that is the angle at which the wing meets the on-coming air) can also be varied to produce lift.

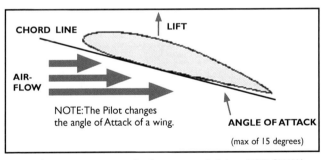

Clearly, if one was to measure the distance travelled along AIRFLOW 'A', and compare it with that travelled along 'B' then one would realise that distance for the first airflow is much greater than the second. But notice they start and finish together.

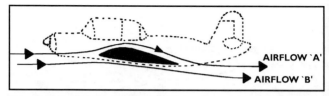

This must mean 'A' travels faster than 'B' in order to finish together because it has to travel a larger distance.

The only way 'A' can travel faster is that the pressure above the wing(path 'A') is reduced and the pressure below the wing is still the same as it was at the start or the finish. This *PRESSURE DIFFERENCE* is known as **LIFT**, and since the pressure at the bottom of the wing is greater than the top, then a rise or lift is achieved.

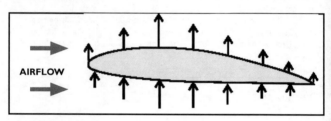

LIFT AND WEIGHT

Consider the cross-section of a typical wing as illustrated below, it can be seen how much LIFT is produced at every point on the wing.
The lift forces are shown in the diagram by the length of the arrows.
Greatest lift is, of course, produced in the middle of the area.

THRUST AND DRAG

Thrust is in fact identical to what is commonly known, in the motor vehicle, as power. Just as a motor vehicle needs to produce continuous power to remain in motion, so too does an aircraft.

DRAG

Any object that moves through the air has to overcome the DRAG or the resistance before it can move in a desired direction. A car experiences two types of resistance. Firstly, there is the friction between the road and the wheels, and secondly, there is resistance from the air. However, in an aircraft only the air resistance need be considered. The more aerodynamic and smooth the surface of an aircraft or a car the less DRAG it produces.

There are three main parts which make-up total DRAG of an aircraft:

1. **Form Drag** - total DRAG caused by the parts of an aircraft.
2. **Skin Friction** - smooth surfaces produce less friction.
3. **Induce Drag** - double the air speed, four times the DRAG; similarly, treble the airspeed, nine times the DRAG, and so on.

LIFT AND WEIGHT IN STRAIGHT AND LEVEL FLIGHT

If the LIFT is greater than the WEIGHT, an aircraft will CLIMB; and if the WEIGHT is more than the LIFT an aircraft will DESCEND. However, in straight and level flight, both the LIFT and Weight are equal.

STALLING

The Stall

Normally, air flows smoothly and continuously over and under the wings in flight, with some amount of Angle of Attack. However, if this angle of attack is increased beyond 15° then the airflow round the wing suddenly becomes turbulent, which causes the LIFT to DECREASE rapidly. This sudden and rapid loss of LIFT is known as the STALL. The result is that the aircraft descends rather quickly causing height loss which in some circumstances could be dangerous.

STALLING SPEED

The stalling angle of a particular aircraft wing does not vary. But, the speed at which a STALL can occur varies from aircraft to aircraft. The stall can occur at high or low speeds.

Factors which influence the stalling speed are:-
1. **WEIGHT** - Higher the weight, higher the stalling speed.
2. **POWER** - Greater the power, lower the stalling speed.
3. **FLAPS** - Lowering flaps reduces stalling speed, especially when landing.
4. **MANOEUVRES** - ALL manoeuvres increase the stalling speed, in particular, steep turns.

NOTE:

Control Column back,	nose up.
Control Column forward,	nose down.
Control Column to the left,	roll to the left.
Control Column to the right,	roll top the right.
Left Rudder,	yaw to the left.
Right Rudder,	yaw to the right.

STABILITY AND CONTROL

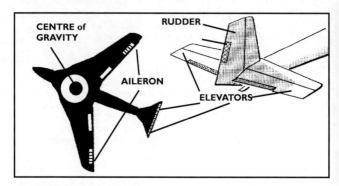

THREE PLANE MOVEMENTS

An aircraft in flight has the freedom to move in three planes or three different ways:
PITCHING plane (lateral axis). ROLLING plane (longitudinal axis) and YAWING plane (vertical axis). Each axis passes through the centre of gravity of the aircraft, and the aircraft can rotate freely in any of these three planes. This is illustrated in the diagram next page.

To achieve movement in any one of these planes described an aircraft has three important 'SURFACES' or 'AREAS' which are used to achieve a required manoeuvre.

The Control Column (commonly known as the 'stick') is linked to two of these surfaces - the ELEVATORS (which produce a PITCHING movement) and the AILERONS (which produce a ROLLING movement.)

The Third surface is the RUDDER (which produces a YAWING movement), and is connected to the RUDDER Pedals.

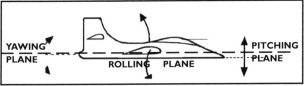

FLAPS

The main purpose of FLAPS is to enable aircraft to make landing approach at as safe and slow a speed as possible. FLAPS are lowered, used, mainly during landing, but can also be used for take-off and are raised when not in use to 'fit-in' with the rest of the wing - giving the best of two worlds.

It will be realised that at say 30°, with increased lift, the stalling speed is reduced and consequently a slower, safer approaching and landing speed is possible. But at full FLAP, say 70° although there is a further reduction in the stalling speed, there is a most definite increase in the DRAG which results in a steeper approach angle and a better view for the Pilot as shown in the diagram, below.

ADVANTAGES OF FLAP

1. Steeper slower approach, better view.
2. Lower touch-down speed, reduced landing run.
3. Braking effective more since low speed.
4. About 15° of Flap makes take-off more efficient.

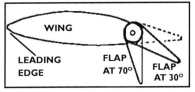

TRIMMING TABS, FLAPS AND SLATS

In the previous pages we explained how varying the position of a surface (the ELEVATORS, AILERONS or the RUDDER), causes the aircraft to move about a particular axis.

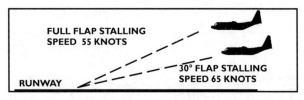

FULL FLAP STALLING SPEED 55 KNOTS

30° FLAP STALLING SPEED 65 KNOTS

RUNWAY

These three surfaces also have additional 'Mini-Surfaces' called TRIMMING TABS, known as the ELEVATOR, RUDDER and AILERON TRIMMING TABS, respectively. These extra parts often play an important role.

TRIMMING TABS

If a Pilot tries to maintain a particular direction by flying 'straight and level' they have to ensure that a 'BALANCED' flight is achieved. This is only achieved if the Pilot is at all time conscious of what is happening to the aircraft, and if it 'DRIFTS' the Pilot has to correct it in order to maintain his FLIGHT PATH.

To relieve the Pilot of constantly having to adjust the aircraft, the Pilot can 'TRIM-OUT' using the TRIMMING TABS to achieve a well balanced aircraft -and now of course the Pilot is free to concentrate on other important activities - such as navigation.

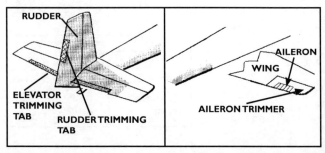

RUDDER

ELEVATOR TRIMMING TAB

RUDDER TRIMMING TAB

AILERON

WING

AILERON TRIMMER

HIGH SPEED FLIGHT - SPEED OF SOUND

You may have noticed that when a batsman strikes a cricket ball there is a delay of a fraction of a second between seeing the ball hit and actually hearing the noise of the strike. Similarly, lightening flashes can be observed several miles away yet the thunder is heard a few seconds later.

When noise is generated, at the source, air is rapidly compressed and pressure waves are formed which travel through the air until they reach the ear - these are known as sound waves. These sound waves all travel at the 'speed of sound'.

Sound Waves travel at different speeds in different air temperature. This can be realised by the fact that temperature of air falls off with height and so does the Speed of Sound. Consider the figures in the table below;

HEIGHT	SPEED OF SOUND
Sea Level	760mph
10,000	735mph
20,000	705mph
40,000	660mph

MACH NUMBER

The Mach Number is the ratio of the true airspeed of an aircraft to the 'LOCAL' speed of sound. If the local speed of sound is 600 mph and the aircraft speed is 1200 then the MACH number is 2 - displayed on a Machmeter.

$$\frac{TRUE\ AIRSPEED}{LOCAL\ SPEED\ OF\ SOUND} = MACH\ NUMBER$$

SOUND BARRIER AND THE SHOCK WAVE

When an aircraft is travelling below the speed of sound, air ahead is 'warned' of a approaching aircraft and makes way by separating so that the aircraft flies through smoothly. If however, the aircraft is travelling at the speed of sound then the air of course has no time to make-way and the effect is that the air strikes the aircraft and noise and vibration can be heard - this is known as the SHOCK WAVE. Furthermore, the higher the speed of the aircraft above the speed of sound the further back the shock is relative to the aircraft.

Some terms commonly used are listed below:

>**SUBSONIC** - under the speed of sound.
>**SONIC** - at the speed of sound.
>**SUPERSONIC** - above the speed of sound.

Gliding

On all aircraft four forces act:

>**LIFT   WEIGHT   THRUST   DRAG**

If any of these forces are disturbed (from a straight and level position) then the aircraft will either climb or descend, accelerate or decelerate. The forces acting on a Glider are the same as those on an aircraft with the engine power reduced to zero.

This means the aircraft or glider will descend, that is GLIDE towards the earth due to it's own weight.

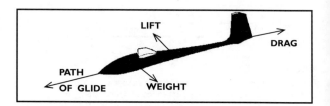

HOW FAR WILL A GLIDER GLIDE

Naturally, the Pilot wants the glider to travel as much distance as is possible. To achieve this, the DRAG factor must be kept to a minimum because this ensures that the ratio LIFT/DRAG is maximum and hence, the further the glider will travel.

This minimum DRAG is attained at a angle of, usually 1 in 19 - that is, at a height of one mile, a glider will travel 19 miles before touch down.

GLIDER LAUNCH

There are several ways of 'launching' a glider;

Aero-Tow - A powered aircraft tows the glider behind it using the tow rope and is released at whatever speed the Pilot choses.

Auto-Tow - A tow rope is attached to a car which is driven at high speed in order to launch the glider.

Bungee - This uses the Catapult principle.

The glider is normally launched at the edge of a slope by a 'V' shaped strong elastic rope - and when released the tension on the rope is enough to raise the glider to a small height.

Winch Launch - This is the most common method used. A powerful winch and engine draws a 1000 yard steel cable to which a glider is attached and quickly launched.

Typically 1000 feet is achieved with a 1000 yard cable.

CONTROL AND INSTRUMENTS

A glider has similar type of control surfaces as any conventional aircraft, and similar controls to operate them.

The instruments usually include: Airspeed Indicator (AI), and of course a Variometer (an instrument which indicates whether an aircraft is rising or descending)

In the cockpit there is also a control which operates the spoilers - these are effectively air brakes.

SOARING

The THERMALS, or rising hot air, is used by glider pilots to remain airborne as long as possible. In fact in a relatively large area there are many thermals, on a sunny day, which a Pilot 'CONSUMES' until a certain height and then moves onto another thermal thus continuously gaining height and in the process remaining airborne for a longer period.

IMPORTANCE OF THERMALS

A THERMAL is a mass (or a quantity) of air which moves upwards when it is warmed for, by example the sun, green fields or lakes (they take much longer to heat than tarmac or built-up areas and these result in thermals being formed as shown in the diagram below.

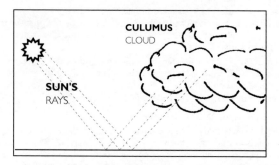

Chapter 10

AIRFRAMES

AIRCRAFT MAJOR COMPONENTS

The 4 main components of a fixed wing aircraft are: Fuselarge, Main Plane, Tail Unit and Alighting Gear illustrated and explained below:

1. FUSELAGE

This is the body of an aircraft to which the other components are attached. It also contains the cockpit or cabin, weapons, fuel tanks avionic and electrical systems and sometimes engines.

The Fuselage accommodates the crew and passengers and may be provided with space for cargo.

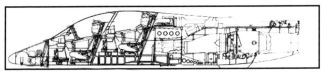

2. MAIN PLANE

The aircraft is fitted with left and right main planes known as wings. The primary function of the wings is to support the aircraft in flight but they may contain or support the fuel tanks, bomb racks, missile rails or in commercial aircraft the engines.

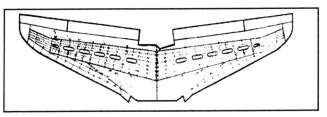

3. TAIL UNIT

This unit is generally made up of the following components:

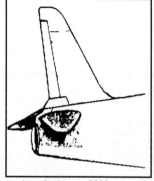

a. TAILPLANE - This is the horizontal stabiliser and prevents the aircraft from pitching in flight. It may consist of a single plane, or seperate left and right planes. It may be fixed, or may be equipped with suitable mechanisms to alter the angle to the airflow in flight.

The tailplane may be mounted at the base of the fuselage, midway throughthe fin, or on top of the fin - giving a 'T' tail configuration.

In some aircraft - particularly delta wings such as the Mirage 2000 - the tail plane is removed completely. in others, for example the Typhoon, the tail plane is replaced by CANNARDS which do the same job as the tailplane, but are mounted forward of the main wings.

b. FIN - The tailfin prevents the aircraft from yawing from left to right during flight. some aircraft, for example the Tornado are equipped with only one fin. Others, such as the FA18 Hornet, F14 Tomcat or Mig-29 Fulcrum are equipped with two tailfins.

c. ELEVATORS - These are hinged surfaces attached to the tail plane which, when operated, cause the aircraft to rise or fall.

d. RUDDER - This is a hinged surface attached to the fin which, when operated, causes the aircraft to turn left or right.

4. ALIGHTING GEAR

This consists of a main undercarriage and a nose or tail wheel undercarriage which absorb the shock of landing and supports the weight of the aircraft when it is on the ground.

AIRPLAIN CONSTRUCTION

Stressed Skin Construction

Almost all aircraft are manufactured to a type of construction known as "stressed skin" which provides a structure with good strength-to- weight ratio. For ease of construction, transportation and repair the airframe is built in sections. The fuselage may consist of nose, front, centre and rear sections which are bolted or riveted together to form the whole. The main advantages of this type of construction are:-

       a. The skin takes the stress in flight.

       b. Relatively lightweight covering providing rigidity.

       c. Provides a good streamlined shape.

In this type of construction the FUSELAGE (see diagram below) consists of *transverse frames or formers* with lengthwise members called *stringers*. The whole is covered with light alloy sheeting.

The frames resist the compression loads and give the fuselage its shape.

The stringers resist the bending loads and provide a means of riveting the skin onto the fuselage.

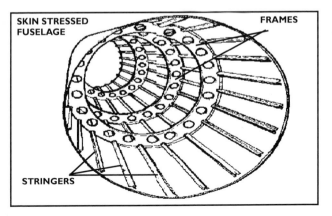

SKIN STRESSED FUSELAGE

FRAMES

STRINGERS

The **MAIN PLANES** have greater thickness at the root (fuselage) end and here the stresses are greater. The wing (see diagram below) is made up of spars which are the main strength members that extend from the root end to the wing tip and resist the torsional loads on the main plane. The ribs provide the wing with the correct aerofoil shape and resist compression loads. The skin covering is riveted to the ribs and stringers.

THE SANDWICH METHOD OF CONSTRUCTION

This is used to cover the main surfaces and consists of inner and outer light alloy sheets attached to a core of corrugated sheet. It provides a rigid structure where heavy spars are not necessary. The number of rivets can be reduced and the surface finish is very smooth.

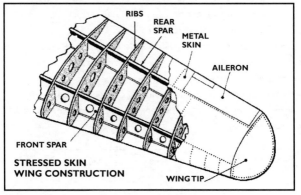

STRESSED SKIN
WING CONSTRUCTION

THE INTEGRAL METHOD OF CONSTRUCTION

This is achieved by machining or chemically etching a solid block of material to provide a skin with integral stringers. This provides a much stronger and more rigid structure without compromising the wing's overall weight.

AIRCRAFT SHAPE AND MATERIALS

The shape of the aircraft since their first flight in December 1903 has changed dramatically from the light wooden framed, linen covered, bi-plane of the Wright Brothers to the gleaming Mach 2+ swept. delta and variable geometry aircraft of the 21st Century.

The biplane was light and slow with a short wing span but a large wing area and therefore great manoeuvrability. The strut and bracing wires between the wings provided a light but strong structure having a low wing loading and hence a safe, low landing speed without resorting to complex flaps and slats arrangement to help generate low speed lift. Unfortunately the early biplane airframes were inefficient at speeds in excess of 150mph, and ultimately replaced by the monoplane.

The monoplane can have a braced or a cantilever (i.e. supported at one end only) type of wing which can be placed high, middle or low on the fuselage.

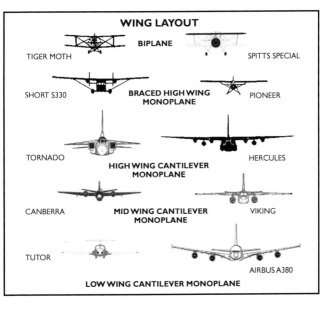

WING LAYOUT

BIPLANE

TIGER MOTH

SPITTS SPECIAL

SHORT S330

BRACED HIGH WING MONOPLANE

PIONEER

TORNADO

HIGH WING CANTILEVER MONOPLANE

HERCULES

CANBERRA

MID WING CANTILEVER MONOPLANE

VIKING

TUTOR

AIRBUS A380

LOW WING CANTILEVER MONOPLANE

Because of the need for greater speed, the monoplane became more complicated and therefore more expensive to build. It required retractable undercarriages, the piston engine was replaced by a turbojet engine and a swept wing became a necessity, all of which increased the weight of the aircraft.

To overcome these problems, the efficiency of the aerofoil needed to be increased, and extra lift inducing devices were needed to be fitted.

Materials have changed significantly over the history of aviation - from the wood and linen construction of the early aircraft, to the light alloys of World War II, and then the steels, fibreglass, carbon fibre, titanium and composites of modern day aircraft. Because of the stresses and strains that are applied to an aircraft in flight, every safeguard is applied and all major components are "lifted" causing them to be replaced after a certain number of flying hours to ensure safety and to extend the life of the aircraft concerned.

ENGINE INSTALLATIONS

When considering where to put the engines on a new aircraft, the designer has to consider a number of factors:-

a. What is the specific role of the aircraft?
b. What are the performance requirements?
c. How many engines are needed to meet the performance requirements?
d. What engines are appropriate to meet these needs, and what are their size and weight?
e. How and where will the engines be mounted?
f. Will this be easy to remove for maintenance and engineering?
g. How efficient is the engine - how much fuel will the aircraft need and where can it be stored?
h. Will the engine(s) positioning affect the centre of gravity
i. Will the engine(s) positioning affect the directional stability of the aircraft?

These, as well as many other questions, will allow the designer to use the most appropriate engine, and in the right place on the aircraft.

Engines can be fitted in the fuselage, outside the fuselage, inside the wings, on the wings or suspended under the wings in pods. In fact they can go in almost any place on an aircraft and have done so over the past 90 years. See illustrations on next page

Engine Positioning

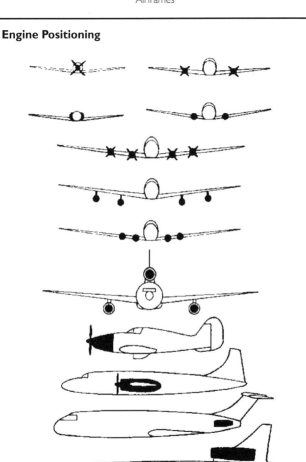

UNDERCARRIAGE

From the skids of early biplanes and gliders, the floats upon seaplanes and through the complex multiwheeled, jockey units of modern cargo aircraft such as the AN225, undercarriages are an essential component of all aircraft. They are required to:-

a. support the aircraft when it is on the ground

b. Keep the engines and sensitive components clear of any obstructions.

c Absorb the shock of landing and provide reasonably smooth taxying.

d. withstand side loads of crosswinds at takeoff and landing.

Modern aircraft tend to have main and nose wheel units and the number of wheels and type of undercarriage leg is dependent on the aircraft's size and role.

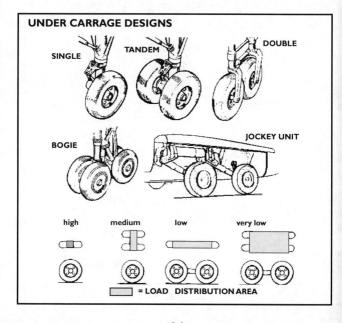

UNDER CARRIAGE DESIGNS

SINGLE   TANDEM   DOUBLE

BOGIE   JOCKEY UNIT

high   medium   low   very low

= LOAD DISTRIBUTION AREA

AIRCRAFT CONTROLS

All aircraft have to be fitted with a system that will enable the pilot to control and manoeuvre the aircraft in flight. There are 3 main control surfaces:-

ELEVATORS on the Tailplane control the **PITCH** axis movement.
AILERONS on the Wing controls the **ROLL** axis movement. **RUDDER** on the Fin controls the **YAW** axis movement.

Depending on an aircrafts shape and configuration some of these control surfaces can be merged - for example Tailerons, Elevons and variable incidence of tailplanes. Canards are another example of where the control surfaces has been moved and no longer fits the traditional aircraft shape - but they still do the job of a tailplane.

The aircraft's control surfaces are operated from the Control Column and Rudder Bar via a number of alternative systems.

- **mechanical linkages** - the control column is linked directly to the control surfaces by cables', the Viking glider is an example of such systems, but it is also used in aircraft such as the Boeing 707.
- **power assisted hydraulics** - The pilot's movement of a control causes the mechanical circuit to open the matching servo valves in the hydraulic circuit. The hydraulic circuit powers the actuators which then move the control surfaces. This arrangement is found in most jet transports and high performance aircraft. These include the Antonov An-225, the Lockheed SR-71 and most aircraft in-between.
- **Fly-by-wire:** (FBW) electronic signals from the control column operate signal transducers which generate the appropriate commands and transmit them to controllers at the control surfaces. This reduces the need for heavy, complex and high maintenance hydraulic systems. An early form of this system was used in the Avro Vulcan. Modern aircraft which use it include Airbus 320 and the Boeing 777.
- **Fly-by-light:** Fly-by-light or Fly-by-optics (FBL) is sometimes used instead of fly-by-wire because it can transfer data at higher speeds, and it is immune to electromagnetic interference. In most cases, the cables are just changed from electrical to fiber optic cables. The data generated by the software and interpreted by the controller remain the same.

As aircraft move towards FBW and FBL systems so the need for heavy mechanical circuits is removed The next step is to eliminate the bulky and heavy hydraulic circuits which move the control surfaces.

The absence of hydraulics greatly reduces maintenance costs, and also decreases the aircrafts overall weight. This system is used in the Lockheed Martin F-35 and in Airbus A380 backup flight controls.

AUTOPILOT

Because of the distances that aircraft travel and the length of time they are in the air, aircrews need to be relieved of the mental and physical strain that occurs in controlling the aircraft. This is the primary function of the autopilot. It is a mechanism that, when switched on, can sense a disturbance of the control surfaces, the aircraft's attitude or heading, and apply immediate counter movements to maintain the course and height set by the pilot.

AIRCRAFT SYSTEMS

Unlike a house, an aircraft is not connected to common services such as electricity, gas or mains water. Therefore each aircraft has to be independent and provide its own services. These cover all aspects of the aircraft's working parts and the following are the major systems involved:

Hydraulics are used for retractable undercarriages, flaps, bomb bays, wheel brakes etc

Pneumatics (or compressed air) has similar uses to the hydraulic systems above, and for the use of control airflow to the wing surfaces to help in improving lift.

Electricals Most aircraft flying today require electrical power and this is usually provided by a generator driven by the aircraft's engine. AC and DC voltages of various frequencies are provided by *Transformers, Rectifiers, Invertors* or *Frequency Changers*. Typical systems requiring electrical power include radios, radar, instruments, actuators and a host of other systems.

Ice Protection When flying in all weather conditions and at high altitudes ice can form on parts of the aircraft. This is particularly dangerous if it forms on the control surfaces or wing as it can change the shape of the aerofoil, so reducing lift, or stop the control surfaces from moving, so stopping the aircraft from changing its attitude. There are four systems employed to prevent ice collecting on an aircraft: **Fluid, Mechanical, Thermal and Electrical.**

Airspeed Indicator: This, as the name implies, gives the pilot his Indicated Air Speed (IAS). This is the speed of the aircraft relative to the air: which it is flowing over it. It is not the aircrafts ground speed - i.e. how fast it is travelling over the ground. IAS is obtained by measuring the air pressure caused by the aircraft's movement.

Altimeter: This instrument gives the height of the aircraft above a certain reference point determined by a known barometric pressure. It measures the difference between the pressures of the free air surrounding the aircraft with-that of the reference point.

Artificial Horizon: By using a gyroscope rotating at very high speed, this instrument will indicate the natural horizon whatever the aircraft's attitude in flight.

Compass: This is one of man's oldest means of navigation. It will give the direction of magnetic north, regardless of the aircraft's attitude.

Other navigation instruments will vary between aircrafts. Some will rely on ground based equipment, whilst others are satellite based - for example an Instrument Landing System (ILS), Automatic Direction Finding (ADF), Distance Measure Equipment (DME) or a Global Positioning System (GPS).

Rate of climb and descent indicator: This instrument gives the pilot an indication of how fast they are descending or ascending.

Turn and slip indicator: This instrument shows the rate of turn. The rate of turn is indicated gyroscopically and the coordination of the turn is shown by an inclinometer, which works in a way similar to a simple pendulum. No pitch information is provided. The rate of turn is the actual rate at which the airplane is rotating.

Other Instruments: A number of other instruments may also be present. These will indicate engine information, include temperatures, engine revolutions, oil levels, pressures. These may also be fuel or battery information present. Other instruments may involve navigation aid, radio and communications.

You should not touch these unless you have been specifically told to do so by the pilot

AIRCRAFT INSTRUMENTS

A description of the numbered instruments shown in the illustration on the previous page are explained in the following numbered paragraphs:

1. AIRSPEED INDICATOR - This, as its name implies, gives the pilot his Indicated Air Speed (IAS) which is the speed of the aircraft in relation to the air which is flowing over it and is not its speed over the ground. IAS is obtained by measuring the air pressure caused by the aircraft's movement.

2. ALTIMETER - This instrument gives the height of the aircraft above a certain reference point determined by a known barometric pressure. It measures the difference between the pressure of the free air surrounding the aircraft and that of the reference point.

3. ARTIFICIAL HORIZON - By use of a gyroscope rotating at very high speed, this instrument will indicate the natural horizon what ever the attitude of the aircraft in flight.

4. COMPASS - This is one of man's oldest means of navigating across the earth's surface. It is therefore not surprising that an aircraft should have one. Other instruments used are aimed at navigation, communication and landing e.g. Instrument Landing System (ILS), Automatic Direction Finding (ADF), Distance measuring Equipment (DME) and in these days of computers and satellites, more and more of this type of electronic equipment is being used.

5. RATE OF CLIMB AND DESCENT - The rate of climb **RoC** is the speed at which an aircraft increases it's altitude.

6. TURN and SLIP INDICATOR - The TURN and SLIP INDICATOR shows the rate and direction of a turn. It tells the pilot if he is performing a coordinated turn using all his controls most efficiently.

Self Test Questions

1. Name the four main components of a fixed wing aircraft.
2. What are the main advantages of stressed skin construction
3. What is meant by the "life" of an aircraft component
4. What are the three main control surfaces on an aircraft
5. Why do modern aircraft need ice protection systems
6. What are the four main instruments used by a pilot
7. Tailplane, Fin, Elevators and Rudder, explain the different controls they have over the aircraft.
8. Name the five Wing Layout designs.
9. Name the different types of Undercarriage designs.
10. What is the primary function of the Auto Pilot
11. How much does a gallon of fuel weight and why is it important
12. What for and when is Auxiliary Power used
13. What is essential to have if you fly over 10,000 feet
14. To what is Indicated Air Speed related
15. When designing an aircraft, what factors have to be considered
16. What is an Undercarriage required to do
17. Where will you find Spars on an aircraft

Chapter 11
PROPULSION

INTRODUCTION

Piston engines have been employed for aircraft propulsion from the earliest days of flying. Today in the Royal Air Force they have been almost totally replaced by gas turbine (jet) engines. After a description of the piston engine, the following will concentrate on the principles of the gas turbine and give examples of their use in the aircraft of today.

THE PISTON ENGINE

This is based upon the four-stroke internal combustion engine. The diagram below shows the four strokes of the sliding piston which harness the power of the expansion of air and fuel vapour when burned in the cylinder.
The crankshaft converts the linear force into a rotary power or torque. The crankshaft is connected directly or via a gearbox to the propeller which then converts the torque into linear thrust.

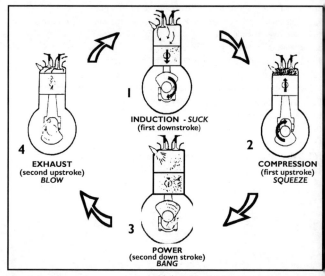

1
INDUCTION - *SUCK*
(first downstroke)

2
COMPRESSION
(first upstroke)
SQUEEZE

3
POWER
(second down stroke)
BANG

4
EXHAUST
(second upstroke)
BLOW

In practice a single cylinder engine as shown would not work as the single power impulse in every two revolutions of the shaft would not produce an even flow of power.

To overcome this, multi-cylinder engine have been developed with cylinders in various layouts. The main configurations are shown in the illustrations on the next page.

THE FOUR STROKE CYCLE

 1. INDUCTION - *(SUCK)* first downstroke. Inlet valve is open. Piston moves down the cylinder, from Top Dead Centre (TDC) to bottom dead centre (BDC).
Fuel air mixture is drawn into cylinder (the charge).

 2. COMPRESSION - *(SQUEEZE)* first upstroke. Both valves are closed. Piston moves back up the cylinder (from BDC to TDC).
Fuel air mixture is compressed into the top of the cylinder (the combustion chamber).

 3. POWER - *(BANG)* second downstroke. Both valves remain closed. Spark occurs igniting the compressed fuel air mixture. Rapid expansion of the burning mixture forces the piston back downthe cylinder from TDC to BDC.

 4. EXHAUST - **(BLOW)** second upstroke. Exhaust valve is open.Piston moves back up the cylinder from BDC to TDC. The burnt (exhaust) gases having now performed their useful work on the power stroke, escape into the atmosphere via the exhaust pipe.

As mentioned on the previous page, the propeller is employed to convert the torque into thrust to propel the aircraft through the air.
The two illustrations on the next page show the mechanics of how this is achieved.

Examples of piston engined aircraft in service today are the TUTOR T1 CHIPMUNK used by Air cadets for Air Experience Flying it is powered by one Lycoming 360 engine.
VIGILANT T1 used by some Volunteer Gliding Squadrons. It is powered by the Grob G2500 engine.

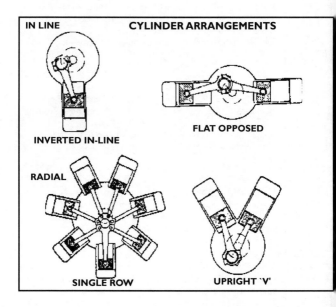

CYLINDER ARRANGEMENTS

IN LINE

INVERTED IN-LINE

FLAT OPPOSED

RADIAL

SINGLE ROW

UPRIGHT `V'

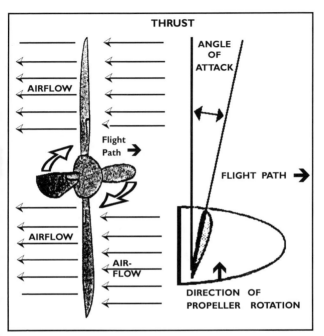

THRUST

AIRFLOW

Flight Path →

AIRFLOW

AIR-FLOW

ANGLE OF ATTACK

FLIGHT PATH →

DIRECTION OF PROPELLER OF ROTATION

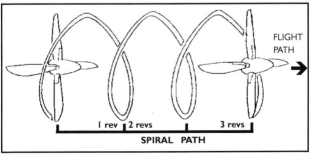

FLIGHT PATH →

1 rev   2 revs   3 revs

SPIRAL PATH

GAS TURBINE ENGINES

In the piston engine petrol vapour and air are burned in the cylinder and the expanding gases move the pistons and the crankshaft to turn the propeller. Towards the end of the Second World war piston engines had come to the end of their development and began to be supplanted by gas turbines (or jets as they have now become known).

The first jet aircraft entering RAF service were the De Haviland Vampire and the Gloster Meteor. These aircraft had no propellers, thrust was obtained from the reaction to the discharge of the stream of exhaust gases from their rearward facing jet pipes.

In comparison to the piston engine the gas turbine power unit is simple. A **compressor** fan blows air into a tubular housing where it is directed to a number of combustion chambers arranged around the central shaft which couples the compressor to a turbine. In the combustion chambers fuel is atomised through high pressure nozzles and mixed with the airflow before being ignited by high voltage electric sparks. Once ignition has been achieved, combustion is continuous provided the fuel supply is maintained. The ignition of the atomised fuel, mixed with the pressurised air, causes a rapid temperature rise and considerable expansion which escapes into the atmosphere via the rearward facing jet pipe.

As the hot gasses escape they pass through the TURBINE which consists of rotating aerofoil section blades fixed radially on a hub at one end of the central rive **SHAFT.** The drive shaft runs right through the engine to the front where it s connected to the compressor fans.

The function of the rearward turbine is to rotate the central drive shaft, the rotation being provided by the exhaust gasses passing over the aerofoil.

This motion translates along the drive shaft to the compressor blades which in turn draws in more air, compressing it and feeding this air into the combustion chamber - and so the cycle starts again.

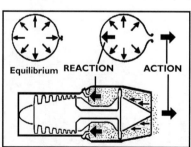

REACTION AND ACTION

These three components (Compressor, Shaft and Turbine) are referred to as a SPOOL. Multi-spool engines have concentric shafts each connecting a compressor to its respective turbine - see the diagram on left.

MAIN TYPES

There are four main types of gas turbine engines.
The first two, **TURBOJET** and **TURBOFAN** are reaction engines that is they derive their power from the reaction of the jet efflux.

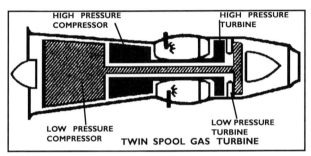

HIGH PRESSURE COMPRESSOR

HIGH PRESSURE TURBINE

LOW PRESSURE COMPRESSOR

LOW PRESSURE TURBINE

TWIN SPOOL GAS TURBINE

The second two, the **TURBOPROP** and **TURBOSHAFT**, operate on an entirely different principle where the energy of the expanding gas stream powers an additional turbine which is connected to a propeller or output drive shaft.

APPLICATIONS OF GAS TURBINE ENGINE TYPES

1. TURBOJET

This is the simplest and earliest form of gas turbine power unit. It is employed mainly in high speed, high
altitude aircraft where small frontal area and high jet velocity are an advantage.
Examples are the 'Olympus 593' in the Concorde and the 'Viper' in various military aircraft.

2. TURBOFAN

This is a "by-pass" engine in which only part of the intake air is fully compressed and passed to the combustion chambers. The remainder is compressed to a lesser degree and ducted round the hot section of the engine to rejoin the exhaust gases in the jet pipe. This gives reduced overall jet velocity, better propulsive efficiency at lower aircraft speeds, lower noise levels and improved fuel consumption.

Examples are the 'RB 211' in the Boeing 747 and 757, the 'Ardour' in the Jaguar and Hawk and the 'RB 199' in the Tornado.

3. TURBOPROP

This is a turbojet with an extra turbine designed to absorb all the energy remaining in the gas stream after sufficient has been removed to drive the compressor. This power turbine drives the propeller through a reduction gearbox. The turboprop is a very efficient engine for relatively low speed, low altitude aircraft - 400 mph, 40,000 feet.

Examples are the 'Dart' in the HS 748 and F27 and the 'Tyne' in the Transall C160 and Atlantic.

4. TURBOSHAFT

This can be considered as a turboprop without a propeller. The power turbine is coupled to a reduction gearbox or directly to an output shaft. As with the turboprop, the power turbine absorbs as much of the remaining gas energy as possible and the residual thrust is very low.

The turboshaft is used extensively in helicopters where the engine drives both main and tail rotors.

Examples are the 'Gem' in the Lynx and the 'Gnome' in the Sea King and Chinook helicopters.

ROLLS ROYCE
Turbofan Engine
Trent 900

VECTOR THRUST

This is a variation of the turbofan where the ability to vary the direction of the jet pipe - and hence the line of action of the resultant thrust. Vector thrusting is employed in a number of aircraft, but is generally associated with VSTOL (Vertical or Short Take Off and Landing) aircraft.

The "Pegasus" turbofan which powers the Harrier has four linked swivelling nozzles which direct the jet downwards for VTOL or through an arc to the rearward position for forward flight - see the diagram below. In the "Pegasus" the fan or by-pass (cool) air is discharged through the two front nozzles and the exhaust (hot) gas through the two at the rear.

Vector thrusting has been developed extensively over recent years to make aircraft more manoeuvrable in flight, enabling them to change direction faster, and at much higher speeds.

Unlike the Harrier, aircraft such as the Su-30 Flanker and the F22 Raptor have 2 and 3-demensional jet pipes in place of conventional jet pipes.

The V-22 Osprey is also a thrust vectored aircraft, but in this case, it's entire turboprop engine rotates around it's wing section to allow it to operate as either a helicopter, or as a conventional aircraft.

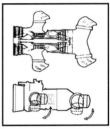

VECTORED   THRUST

V22 OSPREY

RAMJET

The final engine type to be considered is the Ramjet. This is a high velocity, high altitude engine. It is unlike the other engines considered since it has very few moving parts. The ramjet relies on the speed of the aircraft to cause the compression of the air into the engine, doing this by passing it over a cone and into a small opening. Here it is mixed with atomised fuel and passed into an ignition phase in a combustion chamber. The thrust is then provided by exhaust gases through a jet pipe.

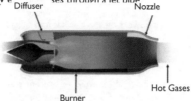

Diffuser   Nozzle

Burner   Hot Gases

The Ramjet requires an aircraft to be at high speeds for it to work efficiently. Ramjet engines are generally found in missiles where they use solid fuel rocket to propel them to speeds where the ramjet engine can work efficiently. An example of this is the Sea Dart surface-to-air missile.

A Ramjet Engine

Self Test Questions

1. What is the drawback with a single cylinder piston engine when used for aircraft power

2. What is the correct name for a 'jet' engine

3. Why does a gas turbine engine have a compressor

4. Why does a gas turbine engine have a turbine

5. What is a 'spool'

6. Name the four types of gas turbine engine, name their applications.

7. What does VSTOL stand for.

8. What does a CRANK SHAFT do

9. How is a CRANKSHAFT connected to the engine.

10. What opens and closes the inlet and outlet valves.

11. What converts TORQUE into THRUST.

12. Name the four types of cylinder aircraft engines.

13. Draw a diagram of of the AIR FLOW across a Propeller.

14. Explain how a gas turbine jet engine compressor works

15. Name a VSTOL aircraft.

16. What aircraft are you most likely to find a Ram Jet engine in service.

17. What do the following have to do with a Piston Engine:
    Suck - Sqeeze -Bang - Exhaust.

18. There are four configurations of piston engine cylinder designs.
    What are each of these cylinder arrangements named.

Chapter 12

METEOROLOGY

METEOROLOGICAL TERMS

ANEMOMETER; Instrument for measuring wind speed.

ANTICYCLONE; A type of pressure distribution in the atmosphere in which a central area of high pressure is surrounded by areas of lower pressure, all pressure measurements being related to the same height above mean sea level.

BACK; Change of wind direction in anti-clockwise sense.

BEAUFORT SCALE; Numerical scale for estimation of wind force varying fro m 0 (Calm) to Force 12 (Hurricane).

CLOUD Main types:-
High Cloud - Cirrus, Cirrostratus, Cirrocumulus.

Medium Cloud - Altocumulus, Altostratus.

Low Cloud - Stratocumulus, Nimbostratus, Cumulus, Cumulonimbus, Stratus.

DEPRESSION; A type of pressure distribution in the atmosphere in which a central area of low pressure is surrounded by areas of high pressure, all pressure measurements being related to the same height above mean sea level.

FOG; Visibility of less than 1,100 yards.

FRONT; Boundary between adjacent air masses characterised by some physical difference, eg. temperature, humidity, etc.

A warm front generally heralds lowering cloud with steady rain and followed by mixed cloudy weather.

A Cold front usually brings turbulent conditions but is followed by clear skies.

INVERSION; Region of atmosphere in which temperature increases with height instead of, as is usual, decreasing with height.

ISOBAR; A line on a weather map drawn through places where the barometric pressure reduced to mean sea level is the same.

LAPSE RATE; The rate at which air temperature decreases with height; the normal value is about 1.7°C per 1000 ft.

OCCLUSION; The meeting of a warm and cold front.

PRESSURE; Atmospheric pressure is usually quoted in inches of mercury or millibars (29.92 ins = 1013.2mb).

These figures are the standard Atmospheric Pressure Settings.

Near sea level pressure drops by approx, 1mb per 30 ft rise in altitude.

VEER; Change of wind direction in clockwise sense.

WEATHER REPORT; Statement of weather conditions existing at a specified place and time.

VISUAL METEOROLOGICAL CONDITIONS (V.M.C.)
Weather conditions are such that flight may be conducted in accordance with Visual Flight Rules.

INSTRUMENT METEOROLOGICAL CONDITIONS (I.M.C.)
Weather conditions are such that compliance with Visual Flight Rules is precluded.

CHART MARKING SYMBOLS

CHARACTER OF FRONT	ON PRINTED CHART	ON WORKING CHART	DIRECTION OF MOVEMENT
Warm		Continuous Red Line	↑
Cold		Continuous Blue Line	↓
Occluded		Continuous Blue Line	↑

A full list of the Symbolic Symbols related to weather charts are available from the Met Office weather site http://www.metoffice.gov.uk/guide/weather/symbols

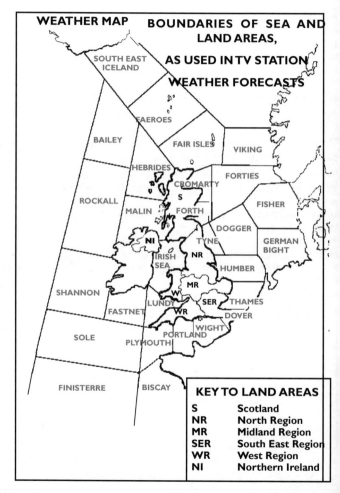

WEATHER MAP   BOUNDARIES OF SEA AND
LAND AREAS,

AS USED IN TV STATION

WEATHER FORECASTS

SOUTH EAST
ICELAND

FAEROES

BAILEY   FAIR ISLES   VIKING

HEBRIDES   FORTIES

ROCKALL   CROMARTY
                S
                MALIN   FORTH   FISHER

                        DOGGER

                NI   TYNE   GERMAN
                IRISH   NR   BIGHT
                SEA

SHANNON   MR   HUMBER

FASTNET   LUNDY   SER   THAMES
                        WR   DOVER

                PORTLAND WIGHT
SOLE   PLYMOUTH

FINISTERRE   BISCAY

KEY TO LAND AREAS

S	Scotland
NR	North Region
MR	Midland Region
SER	South East Region
WR	West Region
NI	Northern Ireland

WEATHER SYSTEMS

On a weather chart, lines joining places with equal sea-level pressures are called isobars. Charts showing isobars are useful because they identify features such as anticyclones (areas of high pressure), depressions (areas of low pressure), troughs and ridges which are associated with particular kinds of weather.

HIGH PRESSURE OR ANTICYCLONE

In an anticyclone (also referred to as a 'high') the winds tend to be light and blow in a clockwise direction. Also the air is descending, which inhibits the formation of cloud. The light winds and clear skies can lead to overnight fog or frost. If an anticyclone persists over northern Europe in winter, then much of the British Isles can be affected by very cold east winds from Siberia. However, in summer an anticyclone in the vicinity of the British Isles often brings fine, warm weather.

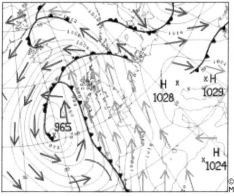

Figure 1.
The chart left shows the flow of wind around a depression situated to the west of Ireland and an anticyclone over Europe.

LOW PRESSURE OR DEPRESSION

In a depression (also referred to as a 'low'), air is rising. As it rises and cools, water vapour condenses to form clouds and perhaps precipitation. Consequently, the weather in a depression is often cloudy, wet and windy (with winds blowing in an anticlockwise direction around the depression). There are usually frontal systems associated with depressions.

A rule in synoptic meteorology, enunciated in 1857 by Buys Ballot, of Utrecht, which states that if, in the northern hemisphere, one stands with one's back to the wind, pressure is lower on one's left hand than on one's right, whilst in the southern hemisphere the converse is true. This law implies that, in the northern hemisphere, the winds blow anticlockwise round a depression, and clockwise round an anticyclone; the converse is true in the southern hemisphere.

ISOBARS (LINES OF EQUAL ATMOSPHERIC PRESSURE)

The lines shown on a weather map are isobars - they join points of equal atmospheric pressure.

The pressure is measured by a barometer, with a correction then being made to give the equivalent pressure at sea level. Meteorologists measure pressure in units of millibars (mb), though instruments sometimes give pressures in terms of inches of mercury. The term hectopascal (hPa) is often used instead of millibar, where 1 millibar equals 1 hectopascal. In the British Isles the average sea-level pressure is about 1013 mb (about 30 inches of mercury), and it is rare for pressure to rise above 1050 mb or fall below 950 mb.

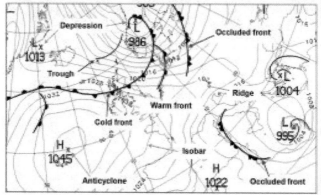

Figure 2*. The chart above shows the association between depressions, anticyclones, isobars and weather fronts.*

© Crown Copyright 2015, the Met Office

Charts showing isobars are useful because they identify features such as anticyclones and ridges (areas of high pressure) and depressions and troughs (areas of low pressure), which are associated with particular kinds of weather. These features move in an essentially predictable way.

Also, wind speeds and directions are related to the spacing and orientation of the isobars.

Relationship between isobars and wind

There are two important relationships between isobars and winds.

> *1. The closer the isobars, the stronger the wind.*
> *2. The wind blows almost parallel to the isobars.*

These make it possible to deduce the wind flow from the isobars.

WIND SPEED AND DIRECTION

The direction given for the wind refers to the direction from which it comes. For example, a westerly wind is blowing **from the west** towards the east. Measurements of wind strength are made at 10 metres (33 feet) above the ground. A specified height has to be used because the wind speed decreases towards the ground. In this country winds are measured in knots (nautical miles per hour). However, forecast winds are often given in miles per hour (where 1 knot is equivalent to 1.15 mph) or in terms of the Beaufort Scale. There are rapid variations in the wind - these are referred to as gusts. Gusts are higher inland than over the sea or windward coasts, although the mean wind speeds tend to be lower inland. Typically, gusts can be 60% higher than the mean speed, although in the middle of cities this can reach 100%. Northerly winds tend to be gustier than southerly ones.

RELATIONSHIP BETWEEN WIND DIRECTION AND WEATHER

In general, the weather is strongly influenced by the wind direction, so information about the wind provides an indication of the type of weather likely to be experienced. However, this approach is effective only if the wind is blowing from the same direction for some time. A marked change in wind direction usually indicates a change in the weather.

Northerly winds tend to bring relatively cold air from polar regions to the British Isles. Similarly, southerly winds tend to bring relatively warm air from the tropics. The characteristics of the air are also affected by its approach to the British Isles. Air picks up moisture if it travels across the sea, but remains relatively dry if it comes across the land.

As cold polar air moves southwards over an increasingly warm sea, the heating of the air by the sea causes cumulus clouds to form. These clouds may grow sufficiently for showers to develop and, consequently, winds from the north-west, north or north-east usually bring cold, showery weather to the British Isles.

Warm air from the tropics moving northwards over the sea is cooled from below. Sometimes the cooling is sufficient for sea fog or a thin layer of stratus to form. The cloud can become thick enough for drizzle, especially on windward coasts and over high ground. In general, winds from the west or south-west are associated with overcast, wet weather.

Winds from the south and south-east mainly occur in summer and these bring warm, dry weather. However, southerly winds can sometimes bring hot, thundery weather.

Easterly winds in winter bring very cold air to the British Isles. The characteristics and path of the air determine whether it is cloudy (with perhaps rain, sleet or snow) or fine and sunny. In summer, an easterly wind will mean it is cool on the east coast but warm elsewhere, usually with clear skies.

FRONTS

The boundary between two different types of air mass is called a front. In our latitudes a front usually separates warm, moist air from the tropics and cold, relatively dry air from Polar Regions. On a weather chart, the round (warm front) or pointed (cold front) symbols on the front point in the direction of the front's movement. Fronts move with the wind, so they usually travel from the west to the east. At a front, the heavier cold air undercuts the less dense warm air, causing the warm air to rise over the wedge of cold air.

As the air rises there is cooling and condensation, thus leading to the formation of clouds. If the cloud becomes sufficiently thick, rain will form.

Consequently, fronts tend to be associated with cloud and rain. In winter, there can be sleet or snow if the temperature near the ground is close to freezing. It is convenient to distinguish between warm fronts, cold fronts and occluded fronts.

A front which is moving in such a way that the warm air is advancing to replace the cold air is called a **warm front**. As the warm front approaches, there is thickening cloud and eventually it starts to rain. The belt of rain extends 100-200 miles ahead of the front. Behind the front the rain usually becomes lighter, or ceases, but it remains cloudy. As a warm front passes, the air changes from being fairly cold and cloudy to

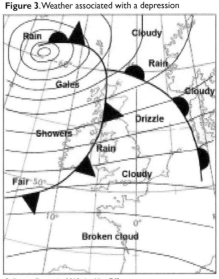

Figure 3. Weather associated with a depression

© Crown Copyright 2015, the Met Office

being warm and overcast (typical of warm air from the tropics travelling over the sea). Also there is a clockwise change in wind direction, and the wind is said to 'veer'.

A **cold front** moves so that the cold air is advancing to replace the warm air. This means that as a cold front passes, the weather changes from being mild and overcast to being cold and bright, possibly with showers (typical of cold polar air travelling over the sea). The passage of the front is often marked by a narrow band of rain and a veer in the wind direction.

An **occluded front** can be thought of as being a result of the warm and cold fronts meeting. Consequently, ahead of an occlusion the weather is similar to that ahead of a warm front, whereas behind the occlusion it is similar to that behind a cold front.

The characteristics given for the fronts apply to active fronts. If the front is weak, the rain associated with it is light or non-existent, and the changes across the front are less marked.

If you would like to learn more about Meteorology in greater detail, go online at **www.metoffice.gov.uk.**

Chapter 13

CADET VOCATIONAL QUALIFICATION ORGANISATION

REAL LEARNING, REAL BENEFITS

CVQO improves the lives of young people and adult volunteers through vocational education (www.cvqo.org)

WHO ARE CVQO?

CVQO is a registered UK charity, offering a broad range of vocational qualifications that are designed to recognise the work undertaken by young people and adult volunteers within youth organisations such as the ACF, ATC, SCC and CCF.

Thanks to CVQO, participants can gain a qualification that validates what they have learned and, while in cadets, increases opportunities to progress to further education or employment.

QUALIFICATIONS FOR CADETS AND ADULT VOLUNTEERS

CVQO qualifications are carefully mapped to the training programmes of the cadet forces, meaning that with only a little extra work on top of their usual activities, cadets can receive something widely recognised by schools, colleges, universities and employers.

CADETS AGED 16-18

For cadets aged 16-18, these include BTEC Level 2 awards in 'Teamwork and Personal Development in the Community' and 'Music for Practical Performance' – both are delivered free of charge by CVQO. There is also the chance to apply for a funded place on CVQO's Leadership course at Outposts, Somerset, in October, gaining an ILM Level 3 in Leadership and Management in the process.
(www.cvqo.org/qualifications/what-we-provide/BTEC)

BTEC LEVEL 1 CERTIFICATE IN TEAMWORK, PERSONAL SKILLS & CITIZENSHIP

Aims and Objectives

The CVQO-led BTEC Level 1 Certificate in Teamwork, Personal Skills & Citizenship has been designed to provide learners with the opportunity to:

- Develop knowledge, understanding and skills that support their personal and career interests into employment
- Develop a range of skills and techniques, personal qualities and attitudes essential for successful performance in education and in working life
- Achieve a nationally recognised Level 1 BTEC qualification• Access programmes of study that can enable progression to higher level qualifications

Entry Requirements

There are no formal entry requirements other than that learners should be aged between 13-15yrs at time of registration. The CVQO-led Edexcel Level 1 Certificate in Teamwork, Personal Skills & Citizenship is aimed at young people who wish to develop their life-skills for further education or the workplace.

Assessment

Learners will be coached and evaluated by trained and accredited assessors as they participate in and successfully complete a range of activities and topics. The assessment will include a mix of observation and demonstration of practical skills, and written and oral questioning on subjects including:

- Developing as a citizen
- Personal fitness
- Maintaining health and wellbeing
- Self-reliance
- Effective communication
- Working effectively with others

What you will gain?

Successful learners will gain an Edexcel Level 1 Certificate in Teamwork, Personal Skills & Citizenship. This qualification has been accredited to the Qualifications and Credits Framework (QCF).

BTEC LEVEL 2 IN TEAMWORK AND PERSONAL DEVELOPMENT IN THE COMMUNITY

The BTEC Level 2 in Teamwork and Personal Development in the Community hones your skills in leadership, teamwork, communications, problem solving, and fitness.

You'll be doing a mix of theory and practical work (including adventure training activities), and come away with really useful life skills too – like how to write a good CV, communication, adventure training, health and nutrition. Best of all, if you're a Cadet over 16 it's free!

To enrol, just contact your local Cadet Headquarters.

BTEC LEVEL 2 IN ENGINEERING

Are you in the Sea Cadet Corps, over 16 and into engineering?

The BTEC Level 2 In Engineering provides a recognised qualification for your achievement in the SCC engineering specialisation. It will also give you a good idea about a job in engineering.

Contact your SCC Engineering Officer for more details of the BTEC and how to get it.

BTEC LEVEL 3 IN PUBLIC SERVICES

The BTEC Level 3 in Public Services is worth up to three A-levels, depending on whether you take the Subsidiary Diploma, Diploma or Extended Diploma.

The course is a mix of theory and practical work covering leadership, teamwork, communications, problem solving and fitness.

You'll learn some great life skills too - citizenship, team leading and government – and enjoy some brilliant outdoor activities while you're at it.

You have to be a cadet over 16 to do the course, and there will be some teaching at school, adventure training activities and some weekend training on top of your usual cadet activities.

This is only available to schools and colleges at present.

BTEC LEVEL 3 IN MUSIC

BTEC LEVEL 3 MUSIC WITHIN THE UNIFORMED PUBLIC SERVICES

CVQO has developed a suite of bespoke qualifications for the exclusive use of the Royal Marines School of Music, Portsmouth and the Corps of Army Music at Kneller Hall. Candidates have the choice of studying towards three separate Diplomas:

- Diploma in Music
- Diploma in Music Leadership
- Diploma in Music Management

Prospective learners should contact their Training Team, Bandmaster or CVQO's Head of Music for further information

BTEC LEVEL 3 IN MUSIC (PERFORMANCE)

This is the newest addition to CVQO's portfolio of music qualifications and is currently being developed. There will be four different tiers available:

- Certificate in Music (Perf) - I AS Level
- Subsidiary Diploma in Music (Perf) - I A Level
- Diploma in Music (Perf) - 2 A Levels
- Extended Diploma in Music (Perf) - 3 A Levels

We are ready to pilot the Certificate in Music (Perf) so check back with CVQO later for an update! *(www.cvqo.org)*

ADULT VOLUNTEERS

Adult volunteers can study with CVQO for a City & Guilds or ILM qualification in Leadership and Management, with the opportunity to celebrate their achievements at one of our prestigious annual graduation events. These are offered at a fraction of the cost of an equivalent commercially available course and go as high as a Level 7 Membership award, equivalent to a Master's degree.

Using their CVQO-led qualifications as a stepping stone, many young learners from the cadet forces have gone on to higher education at university, or achieved successful careers in or out of the armed forces. Adult volunteer graduates have been able to use their awards to achieve promotions or major career milestones.

Adult Awards

Being a great cadet leader is important. It's vital to the high quality training and leadership every cadet receives and it's what makes the Cadet Force such an exciting organisation.

Volunteers come from all walks of life. Some are already highly qualified, others have no formal qualifications. What is certain for all, is that they devote large parts of their lives to making a difference to the lives of others and each individual grows in experience and knowledge as they progress. Through CVQO, that volunteering experience can be formalised with an internationally recognised qualification through City & Guilds or the Institute of Leadership Management (ILM). The CVQO-led programmes range from Level 2 through to Foundation Degree level and on to Master's Degree level, all at a fraction of the cost of commercially available courses. And it's all very achievable with only a modest extra effort. Up to 70% of current volunteering activity within cadet services, for example, can count towards a qualification in leadership and management.

The CVQO Adult Volunteer Development Programme is mapped exactly to cadet volunteering activities and each qualification is recognised by employers.

That's why we believe that a CVQO-led qualification can help make you a better cadet leader and a more valuable employee.
(www.cvqo.org/success-stories)

DUKE OF WESTMINSTER AWARD – REWARDING SELFLESSNESS AND COMMUNITY SPIRIT

Run annually, and supported by the charity's patron, His Grace, The Duke of Westminster, CVQO's most deserving young cadet learners are nominated for our Duke of Westminster Award. The competition seeks to reward our learners not simply for their academic achievements, but for their community spirit, volunteering work and altruistic nature.

After a four-day selection event in Somerset, 24 regional finalists are reduced to nine national finalists and an outright winner. These nine are rewarded with a two-week educational expedition to South Africa.

WHAT TO DO NOW

You will need to prove that your cadet has what it takes to earn a place on the regional finalists selection event.

They need to have shown commitment, drive and determination, and a real interest in their community. They must also be enrolled with CVQO or have previously completed a CVQO-led qualification.

There can be one nomination per squadron, company, sea cadet unit, CCF contingent (or relevant training unit in other CVQO-partnered youth organisations, such as St John Ambulance and Fire Service cadets, Police cadets etc.).

Note:
Nominees must be over
16 on 1 April and under 19 on 1 September
See more at: http://www.cvqo.org/duke-of-westminster

Chapter 14

The Royal Air Force Regiment

IN THE BEGINNING

The RAF Regiment is to the RAF, what the Royal Marines are to the Royal Navy; it is the ground fighting force that enables its parent Service to operate effectively from a safe environment. The RAF Regiment has its roots in the RAF Armoured Car Squadrons that protected the RAF in its Air Control role of preserving the peace of the Middle East Mandate after the Great War of 1914-18. Nos 1 and 2 Armoured Car Squadrons are direct ancestors of today's Nos 1 and II Squadrons RAF Regiment.

2 Armoured Car Company
RAF – HMAC Cerberus RR AC

In the post-war years, the fledgling RAF operated in relatively benign environments; however, the German shock tactics developed in the Spanish Civil War and in the approach to World War II, coupled with the British Army's focus on rebuilding itself after the debacle of the British Expeditionary Force's evacuation from Dunkirk in 1940, forced a different and radical review of RAF ground defence. A specialist RAF 'Ground Gunner' organization was established but its *ad hoc* and ill-defined tactics were no match for the enemy's capabilities.

Prime Minister Winston S Churchill observed, in 1941 – following the Battle of Crete debacle - that, '*Every Airfield should be a stronghold of fighting air-groundmen, and not the abode of uniformed civilians in the prime of life protected by detachments of soldiers*'. Recognizing that the RAF needed its own specialist ground defence force, the RAF Regiment was formed by the Royal Warrant of HM King George VI in February 1942, as a unique Corps within the RAF. While the strategic function of the Corps was to be inherently defensive, it was deemed essential that it should be trained to act tactically on the offensive and that its title should be one which will foster a fighting spirit and high morale and not lay emphasis on the defensive role. Its initial tasks were essentially the ground and low-level air defence of the UK-based airfields facing imminent Nazi invasion. However, the role expanded rapidly to include more offensive action as the direct invasion threat to the UK mainland diminished and the focus moved to mainland Europe, the Middle East and - with the entry of Japan int the war in December 1941 - the Far East.

RAF Regt Armoured Cars in NWE during WWII

THE POST-WAR YEARS

The Regiment served in every theatre of the war and quickly gained a reputation as a highly effective fighting force. It fought in the Battle of El Alamein with the British 8th Army and was present at the final victory over the Axis forces in North Africa. The Regiment then went on to serve with distinction in Italy, Greece and Yugoslavia. It was involved fully in the D-Day landings in June 1944, where the Regiment fought alongside - and frequently in advance of - its sister Army units, providing route defence and securing

German airfields and equipment before they could be destroyed. It also comprised the first Allied forces to enter Denmark. The Regiment also fought a highly successful campaign in Burma and was responsible for maintaining the security of the forward jungle airstrips that were crucial to the air-logistics support of the land forces in the fight against Japanese forces. At its height, the Regiment comprised some 85,000 personnel, but at the end of World War II, its strength was drastically reduced by the wholesale demobilisation of the Wartime armed forces.

In the post war years, despite frequent UK Government and budget threats

RAF Regt – Malaya

to its very existence, the Regiment continued to provide effective defence of RAF assets worldwide. It played a significant part in the RAF Levies (Iraq), RAF Regiment (Malaya) and the Aden Protectorate Levies, which it commanded for a 10-year period. It provided field forces in support of the Army continuously during OPERATION BANNER in Northern Ireland (1969-2007) and deployed its *Tigercat* surface-to-air missile systems to British Honduras (now Belize), Central America, when Guatemala threatened to invade the British Dependency in 1972 and again in 1978. In 1982, No63 Squadron RAF Regiment, armed with the *Rapier* short-range air defence system, deployed with 5 Infantry Brigade to defend the RAF's *Harrier* Force - at Port San Carlos and then Port Stanley - against Argentinean air attack during the Falklands Conflict. Units of the RAF Regiment remained in the Falklands providing continuous, 24-hour air defence of the RAF airfields there for the following 24 years.

The RAF Regiment relinquished its air defence role in 2008, leaving it with its mainstay field squadrons in the infantry role. One unit – No II Squadron RAF Regiment – has a fully-fledged parachute capability to enable it to secure hostile airfields in advance of the land forces. That Squadron is, currently, the only British unit to have parachuted into an active operational theatre - in Sierra Leone - since the Suez Crisis in 1956. Another unit, The Queen's Colour Squadron (No 63 Squadron RAF Regiment) is responsible for the custody and escort of The Queen's Colour for the RAF in the UK. Although technically a RAF unit, it is commanded and manned by the RAF Regiment; it is dual-roled as a field squadron and has been deployed on operations in Cyprus, Iraq, the former Republic of Yugoslavia and Afghanistan.

The RAF Regiment also deployed *en masse* to protect RAF assets during Gulf War 1, the Allied recapture of Kuwait, in 1991 and returned there in 1997 when Iraq once again threatened its neighbours. It was also fully involved in Gulf War II, the invasion of Iraq, and the United Nation's counter-terrorist operation in Afghanistan from 2002. Elsewhere, the RAF Regiment has also provided a significant number of officers in support of United Nations' peace-support and peacekeeping operations; these have included Cyprus, Bosnia-Herzegovina, Kosovo, Cambodia, Sierra Leone, former Soviet Union Republics and many others over several decades. The Regiment is also provides a combat element of the UK Special Forces Support Group and individual personnel in the Special Air Service; it has also participated in a highly effective Officer Exchange Programme with the USAF Combat Security Police and Security Force since 1965. On its formation, the home of the RAF Regiment was at Belton Park, Leicestershire, but it moved in 1946 to RAF Catterick, North Yorkshire, where it stayed until it transferred to its current location at RAF Honington, Suffolk, in 1994. The Corps was presented with its first Queen's Colour by HM Queen Elizabeth II in 1953; since then, four other Queen's Colours for the RAF Regiment have been presented, the last one - together with The Queen's Colour for the RAF in the UK - at RAF Fairford in July 2008, celebrating the 90th Anniversary of the formation

Queen's Colour Presentation at RAF Fairford in 2008

of the RAF. The Corps sets great store in the community of the Regimental Family. Military ethos, traditions and *esprit de corps* are viewed as powerful motivators and are emphasised throughout an individual's time with the Corps and afterwards as a veteran. A competitive spirit is patently visible in all aspects of the RAF Regiment.

CORPS ORGANIZATION

The Corps is commanded from Headquarters RAF Air Command at RAF High Wycombe in Buckinghamshire. At its head is the Commandant General, an Air Commodore. It is a diverse Regiment, since although the majority of its manpower is vested in the RAF's Force Protection Force, many others occupy positions within the wider NATO, Ministry of Defence, Joint Service and RAF operations and training organizations. For example, the RAF Regiment is responsible for the organization and implementation of all RAF station and operational Force Protection training for the RAF. Additionally, it provides the command and core element to the Joint Service (JS) Chemical, Biological, Radiological and Nuclear (CBRN) Defence Centre at Winterbourne Gunner in Wiltshire, and a significant element of the

JS CBRN Regiment at RAF Honington. It also provides other Corps assets in support of UK Special Forces. The RAF Regiment was responsible for developing NATO's *Survive to Operate* (STO) concept for its international air forces; the STO concept was later developed into NATO's and the

General Purpose Machine Gun in the Sustained Fire Role

British Armed Forces' *Force Protection (FP)* concept which provides a comprehensive and coordinated approach to the defence of military assets. The RAF Regiment is widely recognized as the world leader in specialist FP and CBRN operations.

With the loss of the air defence role in 2008, the Regiment is now focussed mainly on providing its infantry capabilities. There are currently seven field squadrons (with an eighth in prospect), all under the operational command of a RAF Force Protection Wing Headquarters and supported by a commensurate number of Royal Auxiliary Air Force (RAuxAF) and RAuxAF Regiment units. Further manpower, equipment and unit enhancements to the Force are planned to cater for the Corps' ongoing operational commitments in Iraq and Afghanistan.

The RAF Regiment, on operations, is primarily responsible for the ground defence of RAF facilities 'outside of the wire' and this role involves the active patrolling and *'domination of ground'* out to a certain distance to deter and prevent hostile forces from launching direct or indirect attacks upon the airbase. Internal base defence is generally undertaken by the wider RAF contingent and the RAF Police, supported by the RAF Regiment. Regiment field squadrons are generally better equipped than their British Army counterparts, notably in the provision of integral indirect fire support (ie mortars) and CBRN areas. Of note, the RAF Regiment is, reputedly, the only force in the British Armed Forces to have been on uninterrupted operations since its inception in 1942.

Queen's Colour Squadron (No. 63 Squadron RAF Regiment) on Parade at Buckingham Palace - 2008

CEREMONIAL DUTIES

Another, more public, role of the RAF Regiment is providing the professional ceremonial support for the RAF. This role is undertaken primarily by The Queen's Colour Squadron (No 63 Squadron RAF Regiment). With its origins in the RAF Regiment's Demonstration Flight and then the RAF Drill Unit, The Queen's Colour Squadron was formed on 1st November 1960 and has since gained a worldwide reputation for drill and ceremonial excellence. It represents the RAF at all major ceremonial occasions and, as mentioned earlier, is the Escort Squadron to The Queen's Colour for the RAF in the UK, whenever it is paraded. The Squadron also provides Guards of Honour for visiting Heads of State and military dignitaries. It also has the honour, since 1943, of carrying out Public Duties on behalf of the RAF at Buckingham Palace, St James' Palace, Windsor Castle and Edinburgh Castle on a regular basis. However, the Squadron is probably best known for its continuity drill displays, which have been performed before audiences throughout the world.

Continuity Drill – the execution of a complex series of drill movements covering foot and arms drill without orders – was pioneered by the RAF Regiment's Demonstration Flight and began life as a training aid; it later evolved into a role for The Queen's Colour Squadron. The displays require the Gunners to memorise several hundred consecutive drill movements, all of which are taken directly from the RAF Drill Manual; none are contrived merely to enhance a performance. The Queen's Colour Squadron currently holds the world record – certified by the Guinness Book of World Records – for completing the most rifle and foot drill movements in a 24-hour period.

INITIAL TRAINING

The RAF Regiment, in concert with British Army Infantry and Royal Marines, only accepts male candidates for service. If you aspire to join the RAF Regiment, you will have to undertake (for commissioned service as an officer) a Potential Regiment Officers' Acquaintance Course – PROAC – or (for non-commissioned service as a Gunner) the Potential Gunners' Acquaintance Course – PGAC – at RAF Honington. Organized through the Armed Forces' Careers Information Offices, these three-day courses would assess your level of fitness and overall suitability for undergoing Regiment training.

For those successful PROAC candidates, initial officer training conducted at RAF College Cranwell would be a pre-cursor to undertaking the Junior Regiment Officers' Course (JROC) but, for those passing the PGAC, initial RAF training is undertaken at RAF Honington before embarking on the professional Trainee Gunners' Course. Both courses would teach you how to operate a variety of personal and section-level weapons, in a wide range of environments and climatic conditions. The training is tough because it has to be. Soon after graduation, you could find yourself in the thick of an engagement with enemy forces in a distant and hostile land; the RAF Regiment trains its people well and effectively to ensure that they have the best advantage in a conflict situation. Those on the JROC also learn to be junior commanders, developing the necessary tactics to enable them to lead their men in combat situations from the outset of their careers. Those who make the grade at the end of the long and arduous courses have the honour of wearing the Corps' coveted RAF Regiment shoulder 'flash'. On completion of the basic RAF Regiment training, individuals will then progress to further training, including specialist communications and 'close precision attack' skills as a Sniper. After graduation, you would find yourself assigned to a RAF Regiment squadron with the prospect of deploying operationally within a short period of time. However, you would return to RAF Honington occasionally to complete further training.

The RAF Regiment is fiercely proud of its heritage and its reputation for its world-class Force Protection capabilities. Do you have what it takes to serve in the RAF Regiment? For more details contact your local Armed Forces' Careers Information Office or go on-line at: www.raf.mod.uk/rafregiment for an interactive look at the Corps.

THE GUINNESS BOOK OF WORLD RECORDS

The Queens Colour Squadron appears in the Guinness Book of Records having completed over 2,700,000 foot and rifle drill movements in 23 hours and 55 minutes. This still stands as a record that, unsurprisingly, has not been challenged.

Picture of the Al Waki firefight in Basrah, Iraq, in which Cpl David Hayden won the Military Cross

Self Test Questions

1. After the Great War of 1914-18 what was the role of the Regiment.
2. How was it equipped to carry out its operational role.
3. When was the RAF Regiment formed.
4. What was thought to be its original task.?
5. In WW2 what battle in North Africa did the Regiment take part.
6. In June 1944 Europe which Army did the RAF Regt serve with.?
5. When was number No63 Squadron equipped with a short-range air defence system.
6. What was the name of the weapons used for short-range defence.
7. Who did the Regiment serve with during the Falklands conflict.
8. What was essentially their role in the Falklands.
9. Which Squadron of the RAF Regt served in the Falklands.
10. Name five theatres of operation that the Regt has served.?
11. Which is the RAF Regt parachute Squadron, and where is it based.?
12. Which is the Queens Colour Squadron.
13. What is the RAF 'STOC' what is its role.?
14. Where is the current home of the RAF Regiment.
15. When was the first Queens colour presented to the Regiment.
16. On what date was the Air Defence role transferred to the Army Royal Artillery.
17. At present there are seven field Squadrons, under whose operational command are they.
18. The Regiment on operations what is their primary responsibility.
19. When was the Queens Colour Squadron formed.
20. What is the purpose of PAGC training.?
21. What is a 'TG' course and how long does it last.?

Chapter 15

Pastoral Care, Discipline and Safe Guarding

ETHOS AND VALUES

The role of the Royal Air Force, in conjunction with the other UK defence organisations, is to deliver the UK defence vision:

- Defend the UK and its interests.
- Strengthen international peace and stability.
- Be a force of good in the world.

- We achieve this aim by working together on our core task to produce battle-winning people and equipment. The Royal Air Force will build upon the successes of our past and on the characteristics that make air power essential across the full spectrum of operations in order to contribute to the Defence Vision.
- Our people lie at the heart of this capability. We rely upon their professionalism, dedication and courage. We must train them well and enable them to leverage the potential of technology to achieve our vision of:
- "An agile, adaptable and capable Air Force that, person for person, is second to none, and that makes a decisive air power contribution in support of the UK Defence Mission."
- "The distinctive character, spirit and attitude of the RAF which together inspire our people to face challenge, and, on occasion, danger. It is underpinned by tradition, esprit de corps and a sense of belonging. It encompasses the will to contribute to the delivery of effective air power that arises from confidence in the chain of command, trust in colleagues and equipment, respect for individuality, sustainment of high professional standards and the courage to subordinate personal needs for the greater good."

As members of the Air Cadet Organisation we all need to aspire to the above.

THE AIR CADET ORGANISATION – COMMANDANT'S INTENT

It is the intent of Commandant Air Cadets to ensure that the ACO:

- Is the uniformed youth organisation of choice for teenagers.
- Provides opportunities for adult volunteers in personal development whilst making a difference to the lives of our youth.
- Is conducted legally, safely and in accordance with best practice.
- Is modern, flexible and committed to continuous improvement.
- Offers opportunities to all in an environment respect equality and diversity in accordance with the RAF Equal Opportunities directive.
- Has a strong corporate identity and engages widely throughout the UK.
- Fosters leadership and good citizenship founded on commitment and self discipline.
- Offers value for money focusing on maximising cadet experience whilst minimising costs.

> "The ethos of the Air Cadet Organisation (ACO) is distinctive character, spirit and attitude of the Corps which together inspire people to pursue the spirit of adventure while providing a framework upon which to build sound moral principles and develop the desire for achievement and self-improvement and thereby provide example and leadership for the young people of the country."

AIR CDRE D MCCAFFERTY - VALUES OF THE ACO

- **Respect** – both self and mutual

- **Integrity** – always

- **Service** – service before self

- **Excellence** – striving for excellence

VISION OF THE ACO

> "To ensure that the Air Cadet Organisation continues to flourish and to remain true to the ideals laid down in its charters, particularly the provision of dequate aviation and other challenging activities to enable it to attract and retain membership and thereby provide example and leadership for the country's youth."

MISSION STATEMENT

> "To sustain a vibrant and effective ACO in an ever changing society supported by trained and committed staff."

THE AIR CADET CODE OF CONDUCT – PERSONNEL INSTRUCTION 501

This document is there for every cadet and cadet's parents to view. Just speak to your Commanding Officer.

PI 501 includes –

- Clarification of ages for cadets
- Introduction of 'Cadet Code of Conduct'
- Guidance regarding cadets with disabilities
- No need to leave on pregnancy
- Revised application for over-18s
- Clarification of CRB requirements
- Requirement for cadets to report arrests etc
- New range of sanctions
- Leaving the ATC

- Complaints

- Speaking Out

  - Pers Form 40

    - APPLICATION FOR AN EXTENSION OF ATC CADET SERVICE BEYOND 18 YEARS OF AGE

  - Pers Form 41

RECOMMENDATION FOR THE DISMISSAL OF A CADET FROM THE ACO

Details

- *Upon becoming a member of the ATC all cadets are committing themselves to following this Code of Conduct and all cadets are required to:*
  - Set an example they would wish others to follow and treat everyone with equal respect and dignity.
  - Respect and be sensitive to individual beliefs, faiths and religions.
  - Respect each others' rights to privacy.
  - Not make fun of anyone else because of their colour, race, religion, abilities or disabilities.
  - Keep others informed of where they are and what they are doing whilst engaged on ACO activities.
  - Attend squadron parade nights at the specified times on a regular basis, unless leave of absence has been previously authorised by the Sqn CO.
  - Not leave an air cadet activity without permission from an adult member of staff.
  - Abide by all air cadet orders when undergoing air cadet activities.
  - Work as part of a team.
  - Listen to fellow cadets and adult members of staff.
  - Report any concerns they have about the way a fellow cadet is being treated either during an air cadet activity or at home, to an appropriate adult member of staff.
  - Show understanding and sensitivity to others.

- *Whilst encouraging the maximum participation possible of young people with special needs and chronic conditions in ACO activities, it is recognised that the acceptance of individual cadets must be*
    - At Sqn CO's discretion, depending upon the facilities and staff available in squadrons
    - As well as an individual applicant's particular needs or conditions.
    - But the ACO has general legal liabilities under the headings of criminal law, duty of care (to CFAVs, cadets and the public), child protection and health and safety.
    - However, the ACO has no legal liability or obligation to provide a particular level of support for a cadet with a specific learning difficulty, disability and/or chronic condition, other than in a health and safety/general duty of care context.

- *Before accepting such an applicant into a squadron, the CO is to:*
    - Establish parents/carers the boundaries of the applicant's involvement in ACO activities and their own involvement in the cadet's activities and ensure they understand both. Discussions of this nature with parents/carers need to conducted sensitively and should ideally be conducted by the Sqn CO supported by a Wing Staff Officer (WSO) (or OC Wing in very difficult or sensitive cases).
    - Obtain a written report (at the parents'/carers' expense where applicable) on the young person from the applicant's doctor stating clearly the limits to be placed on their activities and any special precautions to be taken.
    - Consider whether or not a formal risk assessment is required by the Regional Health and Safety Adviser.
    - Ensure that all appropriate persons in the squadron are made fully aware of the circumstances of, and any treatment prescribed for, any cadets with disabilities or chronic conditions, and actions to be taken in an emergency.

PREGNANCY

- *Health and safety considerations are paramount when dealing with pregnant cadets.*

- *Therefore, in the interests of the mother-to-be and/or her unborn child*

- *Pregnant cadets will only be permitted to continue attending ACO activities as long as there is no risk to the health of either.*

- *When pregnancy becomes known, the cadet must tell her Sqn CO.*

- *The Sqn CO will notify the ACO HS&E Adviser (through WHQ) and arrange for a risk assessment to be created in accordance with JSP 375, Volume 2, Leaflet 36.*

CLARIFICATION OF AGES

- *Year 8 or 13 to 18*

- *Extendable to 20*

- *Can join up to 17th birthday*

- *Exceptionally, a cadet over the age of 17 may re-join the ATC once they have left, subject to Rgnl Comdt's approval*

CONDITIONS OF EXTENSION BEYOND 18

- *Need BASIC and DBS*

- *Meet specific criteria –*

- *Achieved the Leading Cadet classification.*

- *Possess a specific skill that adds value to the ATC, such as:*

- *Flying and gliding; VGS Staff Cadet, AEF Staff Cadet, GS (solo), Flying Scholarship, Pilot Navigation Scholarship, Gliding Instructor*

- *Shooting; any training or supervisory qualifications.*

- *Adventure training; any recognised instructional or supervisory qualifications*

- *Ground training;* qualifications or skills in first aid, food handling, radio communications, BTEC in Aviation Studies or Public Services, musical instruments, leadership, information technology

- *Sport;* qualifications in coaching a specific sport or a Community Sports Leader's qualification

- *Submit a Pers Form 40 (Application for an Extension of ATC Cadet Service over 18 Years of Age)*

- *Approved by Sqn CO and OC Wg*

- If a cadet has not met the all of the pre-requisite criteria OC Wg may, at their discretion and on a case by case basis, appoint a cadet as a staff cadet providing the cadet has passed BASIC and obtained an enhanced criminal records check before their 18th birthday

- *Cadets of 18 and 19 are "Staff Cadets"*

- *Wear an epaulette with "Staff Cadet" and their NCO rank badge*

- *Staff cadets, except when undertaking supervisory duties, should, where possible, be accommodated in alternative accommodation to younger cadets. Where available, this may be in junior ranks accommodation, including transit accommodation.*

- *Cadets aged 18 and over in England and Wales may continue to attend ACO activities*

  - Provided that their PersForm 40 has been approved by OC Wg and their completed CRB application has been submitted to DBS (EA(D)S Cheadle Hulme

  - They are not to be permitted unsupervised access to cadets under the age of 18 until their clearance has been confirmed.

  - *Cadets who have not completed a DBS application form before their 18th birthday are to be excluded, without prejudice, from all ACO activities until they have applied.*

- Any cadet who is:

  - Arrested

  - Issued with a warrant for arrest

  - Is under investigation by the police or social services

  - Who is officially informed that a charge is to be preferred against them

  - Is convicted of a criminal offence or receives a police caution, warning, reprimand or fixed penalty notice

  - Is the subject of any child protection concern (eg by a professional body, primary employer or educational establishment)

  Must inform their Sqn OC Immediately.

LEAVING THE ACO

- *An individual will cease to be a cadet member of the ATC in any of the following circumstances:*
  - At his or her own request.
  - On reaching the age of either 18 or 20, depending on whether the application for an extension of service has been granted in the former case.
  - When joining the Armed Forces, or their Reserves or Auxiliaries.
  - If he or she has not attended a parade for 2 months, unless there are extenuating circumstances, eg exclusion without prejudice.
  - On being dismissed for serious misconduct.

COMPLAINTS

- *Complaints, disagreements and disputes should be resolved informally at the lowest possible level if at all possible.*
  - A cadet who thinks him or herself wronged may report the matter direct to the Sqn CO.

      – If a cadet thinks he or she has been wronged by his or her Sqn
        CO the complaint may be reported to the OC Wg

      – If still unhappy with the outcome, to the Regional Commandant.

- *Any member of the ACO is required by ACP 4 to report any suspicions or evidence of abuse or harm concerning a child whether it is within or outside the ACO.*
  - No-one should feel, or be made to feel, uncomfortable, bullied or intimidated by doing so or being coerced into not reporting them.
  - Cadets should feel comfortable and free to report, at any time, any child protection concerns within or outside the ACO to any member of staff and all commanding officers are to endeavour to create a culture to ensure there is some means for cadets to do so.
  - Cadets should know to whom they should report concerns and also what is likely to happen as a result – they must have confidence that they are being listened to.
  - In addition to support within the sqn, contact details for the NSPCC ChildLine are to be prominently displayed.

- If in doubt – look it up

- If still in doubt ask your Sqn OC

CHILD PROTECTION AND SAFEGUARDING
Duty of care

- There are two aspects of Duty of Care:
  - Moral
  - Legal

- The ACO takes both seriously.

- Duty of Care applies to both yourself and your colleagues, not just to cadets.

AGES OF RESPONSIBILITY – WHAT THE LAW SAYS

- *UN Charter on Children states anyone under the age of 18 is a child.*

- **Under 10 years:** no criminal responsibility.

- **10 to 14 years:** may be held responsible depending the severity of the crime.

- **14 plus:** fully liable for all criminal action.

- Under 16s cannot:
    - Consent to sex
    - Marry
    - Ride a moped

- Aged 17 plus can:
    - Drive a car
    - Ride a light motorcycle
    - Possess a crossbow or firearm

- Aged 18 plus can:
    - Vote
    - Obtain credit
    - Purchase:
        - Alcohol
        - Cigarettes
        - Tattoos
        - Lighter fluids
        - Blades

CP4 SAFEGUARDING AND CHILD PROTECTION POLICY

Policy Statement

"It is the primary responsibility of all adult members of the ACO to safeguard the moral, psychological and physical welfare of children regardless of gender, religion, race, ability, disability, sexuality and social background by protecting them from any form of physical, emotional and sexual abuse or neglect."

> "All children have the right to protection from all forms of abuse and harm when engaged in ACO activities and when in contact with members of the ACO. All adult members of staff have a duty of care, which makes them responsible both for safeguarding children in their care from abuse and harm and for responding swiftly and appropriately when suspicious or allegations of inappropriate behaviour arise."

WHAT TO DO IF YOU YOURSELF OR A FELLOW CADET HAS A SAFEGUARDING ISSUES

- *Refer to ACP4 Child Protection Guide and the Yellow Card issued by HQAC t Staff and Adult Staff Cadets*

- *The Sqn OC.*

- *If the problem does involve another cadet, member of staff or anyone directly connected with the ACO then the OC and WSO must be advised immediately.*

- *Depending on the problem, there are many helplines available to get advice from.*

- *The NSPCC Child Protection Helpline – 0808 800 5000.*

- *Your Wing Executive Officer at your WHQ*

- *Your Sector Commander or Wing CP Advisor – available on cpa.XXXXX@airacdets.org*
  XXXXX indicates the name of your wing.

- Your Squadron Chaplain

SOCIAL NETWORKING POLICY

- *It is inappropriate for adult staff to be 'friends' with cadets on social networking sites. This also applies to cadets adding an adult member of staff as a 'friend'. The only exception is for members of the same immedia family.*

- *Cadets over the age of 18 years may remain 'friends' with cadets under 18, but they must be acutely aware that they must show a good example to younger cadets.*

- *Contact between a member of adult staff and a cadet should only be made in a visible area of an official site or group. Cadets and staff may, however, be members of the same online group.*

- *Any member of the ACO must not bring the organisation into disrepute, either through comments or actions made online.*

- *All personnel should be aware that social networking has led to a number of high profile and localised episodes of bullying and exclusion, as well as sexual grooming in the UK, particularly amongst young people.*

- *Any member of the ACO found to be taking part in such actions may face disciplinary or administrative action and could have their service terminated.*

- *All members of the ACO should be aware that texting on mobile phones between cadets and adult volunteers or permanent staff and vice versa is not advised unless for official business (e.g. timings of an event).*

- *Above all, remember to:*

  - Follow the same standards of conduct and behaviour online as would be expected elsewhere.

  - Always maintain personal information privacy and security.

  - Get appropriate authorisation, where required, from the chain of command.

- *Personnel who breach these guidelines may find themselves the subject of an internal investigation and/or administrative action.*